Scott, Foresman Reading

Crystal Kingdom

Program Authors

Ira E. Aaron
Dauris Jackson
Carole Riggs
Richard G. Smith
Robert J. Tierney

Book Authors

Joanna Cairns
Elizabeth Galloway
Robert J. Tierney

Instructional Consultants

John Manning
Dolores Perez

Scott, Foresman and Company
Editorial Offices: Glenview, Illinois

Regional Offices: Palo Alto, California
Tucker, Georgia • Glenview, Illinois
Oakland, New Jersey • Dallas, Texas

ACKNOWLEDGMENTS

Text and illustration developed and produced by Curriculum Concepts, Inc. under the direction of Scott, Foresman and Company.

"Benjamin Dilley's Thirsty Camel" is an adaptation of BENJAMIN DILLEY'S THIRSTY CAMEL by Roger Bradfield. Copyright 1967 by Rand McNally & Company and used with their permission.

"Eletelephony" from TIRRA LIRRA by Laura E. Richards. Copyright 1930, 1932 by Laura E. Richards. By permission of Little, Brown and Co.

"Mr. Egbert Nosh" from MR. EGBERT NOSH by Paul Groves. Text copyright © 1970 by Paul Groves. Published by Brockhampton Press, now Hodder & Stoughton Children's Books, and used with their permission.

Abridged and adapted from GABRIELLE AND SELENA, text copyright © 1968 by Peter Desbarats. Reprinted by permission of Harcourt Brace Jovanovich, Inc. and Curtis Brown, Ltd.

"Fidelia" is an abridgment and adaptation of FIDELIA by Ruth Adams. Copyright © 1970 by Ruth Adams. By permission of Lothrop, Lee & Shepard Co. (A Division of William Morrow & Company).

"Listening to Music" is reprinted by permission of E. P. Dutton from RHYMES ABOUT US by Marchette Chute. Copyright © 1974 by Marchette Chute.

"The Surprise Party" is adapted by permission of Pantheon Books, a Division of Random House, Inc., from THE SURPRISE PARTY, by Annabelle Prager. Copyright © 1977 by Annabelle Prager.

Adapted by permission of Scholastic Book Services, a Division of Scholastic Magazines, Inc. from KID DYNOBITE by Madeline Sunshine. Copyright © 1978 by Madeline Sunshine.

ISBN 0-673-14810-6

"Mrs. Ling's Cat" is an adaptation of Chapter Two from JOHNNY HONG OF CHINATOWN by Clyde Robert Bulla. Copyright 1952 by Clyde Robert Bulla. By permission of Thomas Y. Crowell, Publishers.

"Cat Bath" from MY CAT HAS EYES OF SAPPHIRE BLUE by Aileen Fisher. Copyright © 1973 by Aileen Fisher. By permission of Thomas Y. Crowell, Publishers.

"Kate's Swimming Pool" is adapted from KATIE'S SWIMMING POOL FOR SPARROWS by Barbara Owen Webb. Reprinted from Humpty Dumpty's Magazine by permission of the author. Copyright © 1976 by Parents' Magazine Enterprises, a division of Gruner + Jahr, U.S.A., Inc.

Adapted with permission of Macmillan Publishing Co., Inc. from GRANDPA, ME AND OUR HOUSE IN THE TREE by Barbara Kirk. Copyright © 1978 by Barbara Kirk.

Adaptation of GIANTS ARE VERY BRAVE PEOPLE by Florence Parry Heide. Text copyright © 1970 by Florence Parry Heide. By permission of Parents Magazine Press and Curtis Brown, Ltd.

"Don't Hide" from SCARY THINGS by Norah Smaridge, Copyright by Norah A. Smaridge and used with her permission.

"Beech Leaves" from THE WANDERING MOON by James Reeves. Reprinted by permission of the publishers, William Heinemann Ltd.

"Angela and the Bear" is adapted from ANGELA AND THE BEAR by Susan Jeschke. Copyright © 1979 by Susan Jeschke. Reprinted by permission of Holt, Rinehart and Winston, Publishers.

"Crayons" is reprinted by permission of E. P. Dutton from RHYMES ABOUT US by Marchette Chute. Copyright © 1974 by Marchette Chute.

"The Spider Plant" by Yetta Speevack from THE SPIDER PLANT is reprinted by permission of Atheneum Publishers. Copyright © 1965 by Yetta Speevack.

Adapted from NOTHING MUCH HAPPENED TODAY, © 1973, by Mary Blount Christian, a Young Scott Book, by permission of Addison-Wesley Publishing Company, Inc.

"Navajo Pet" from NAVAJO PET by Patricia Miles Martin. Text copyright 1971 by Patricia Miles Martin. Published by G. P. Putnam's Sons, 1971. Used by permission of the author.

(Acknowledgments continued on page 320)

CONTENTS

SECTION TWO

SECTION ONE

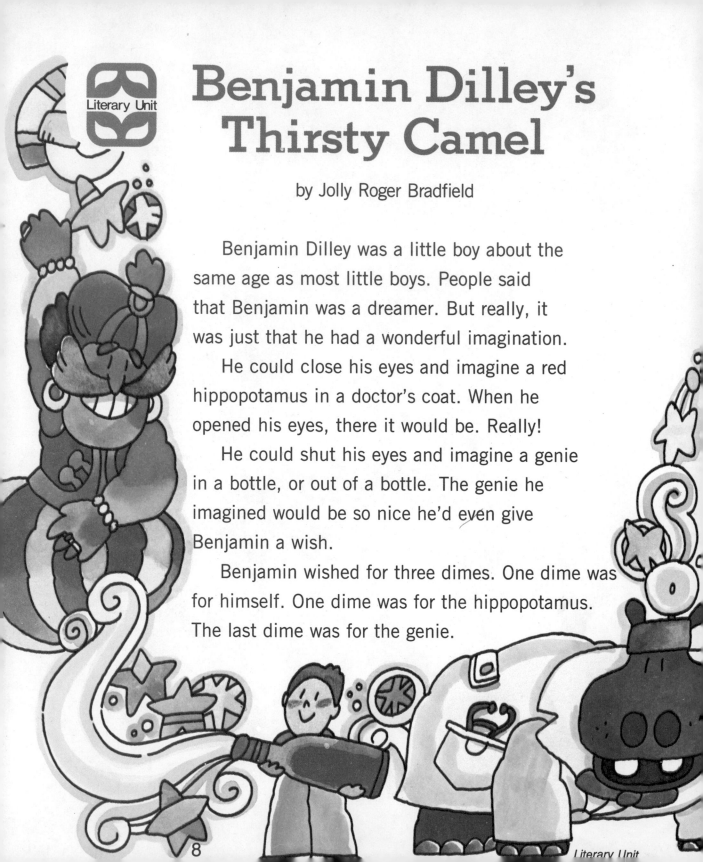

Benjamin Dilley's Thirsty Camel

by Jolly Roger Bradfield

Benjamin Dilley was a little boy about the same age as most little boys. People said that Benjamin was a dreamer. But really, it was just that he had a wonderful imagination.

He could close his eyes and imagine a red hippopotamus in a doctor's coat. When he opened his eyes, there it would be. Really!

He could shut his eyes and imagine a genie in a bottle, or out of a bottle. The genie he imagined would be so nice he'd even give Benjamin a wish.

Benjamin wished for three dimes. One dime was for himself. One dime was for the hippopotamus. The last dime was for the genie.

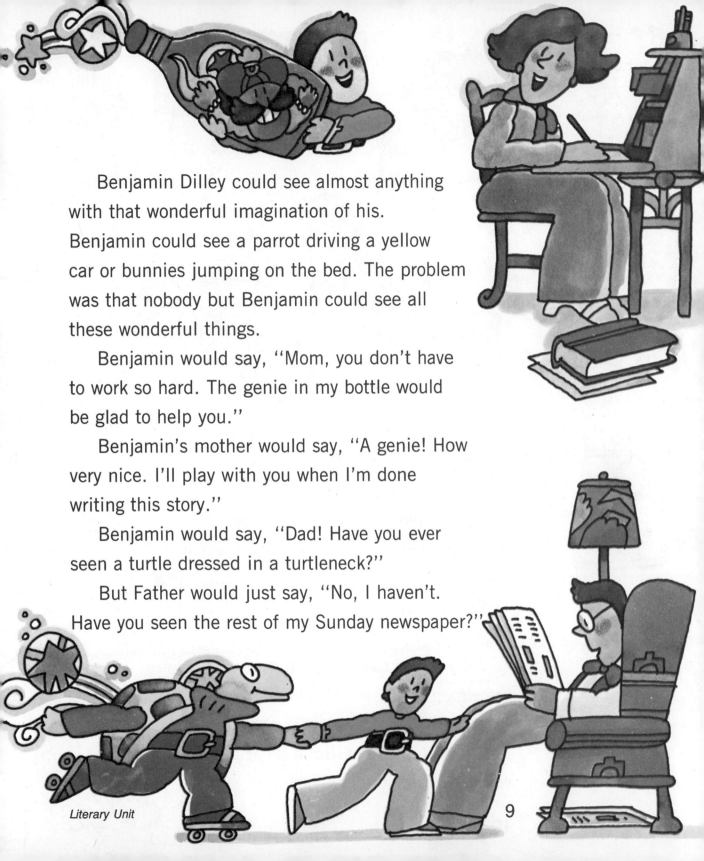

Benjamin Dilley could see almost anything with that wonderful imagination of his. Benjamin could see a parrot driving a yellow car or bunnies jumping on the bed. The problem was that nobody but Benjamin could see all these wonderful things.

Benjamin would say, "Mom, you don't have to work so hard. The genie in my bottle would be glad to help you."

Benjamin's mother would say, "A genie! How very nice. I'll play with you when I'm done writing this story."

Benjamin would say, "Dad! Have you ever seen a turtle dressed in a turtleneck?"

But Father would just say, "No, I haven't. Have you seen the rest of my Sunday newspaper?"

One Sunday, Benjamin was watching his father fix a leak in a pipe in their basement. It was just a small leak. But still, it was taking Benjamin's father a long while.

As Benjamin waited, he used his wonderful imagination. He imagined a funny old camel. The camel had glasses sitting on the end of his nose.

"My camel says you're turning that pipe the wrong way, Dad," said Benjamin.

"Your father knows what he's do—" his father started to say. But a great gush of water stopped him.

10

The water rushed out of the pipe. It was awful! It splashed all over Father. It splashed all over Benjamin. It splashed all over the basement floor. Soon the whole basement was filling up with water.

"It's a flood!" cried Benjamin's father. "It's an awful, awful flood!" He let go of the pipe. Then he splashed up the steps.

Benjamin could hear his father as he yelled into the telephone, "Help! Send a plumber over right away! Send two plumbers, and make it fast! There's a flood in my basement!"

Benjamin looked at the water rushing all around him. He was getting worried.

"Do something, Mr. Camel!" he yelled.

"Glad to," said the camel.

First the camel found Father's tools. He used
one to turn the pipe. (He turned it the way he
had wanted Father to turn it.) He was able to
stop the enormous rush of water almost at
once. Then he did a wonderful thing. . . .

He started to drink. He kept drinking and
drinking and drinking.

"Wonderful water you have here," he said.

As he kept drinking, the funny old camel
started filling out. He got bigger and bigger
and bigger. Soon the basement was almost dry.

The camel was drinking up the last few drops of water when Father and Mother came rushing in. Each carried a big mop. Each looked worried.

"Everything is all right now," the camel said.

Benjamin's father didn't hear him.

"The water is gone!" he cried. "Everything is dry!"

"It should be dry," said the camel. "I've been drink—"

But Father didn't hear. "I don't get it," he cut in. "I just don't get it!"

Just then, the plumber was at the front door.

The plumber walked in. He was followed by two other plumbers.

"Where is the flood?" he yelled.

"My camel has been drinking it up," said Benjamin. But no one listened.

The plumber looked around at the dry basement.

"I thought you said it was filling up with water," he went on.

"It *was* filling up with water," Father answered.

The plumber looked around. Finally, he spotted a small drain under a table. He eyed it in great surprise.

14

"Somehow the water must have all gone down that little drain," he said.

"Oh, yes," said Father.

"Oh, yes," said Mother.

And that was that!

Benjamin was really surprised. Not one of the plumbers had seen his camel. Camels are pretty big. And this one, with all that water in him, was the biggest one ever! Benjamin thought that if the plumber could see that little drain, he should be able to see a great big camel. It really worried him.

Just to make sure, he imagined a whole tree full of owls in front of the plumber.

The plumber didn't see them.

Benjamin imagined a horse playing a horn. It played right near the plumber's ear.

The plumber didn't see it or hear it.

Finally, he imagined a frog. The frog jumped around the basement, coloring everyone blue.

Nobody saw it. Not even Mother, who often said that blue was the color she liked most.

When the plumbers had left, Benjamin's father sat down.

"What a Sunday!" he said. "Without that little drain, we would have had the biggest flood ever!"

Benjamin patted the camel. "Don't you care," he whispered. "*I* know you did it."

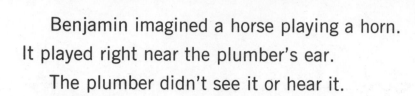

16

That night when he was in bed, Benjamin Dilley imagined the camel on one side of the bed. He imagined the genie on the other. Then he imagined some owls and some bunnies.

"Good night," said the camel, the genie, the owls, and the bunnies.

Then they all went to sleep.

Comprehension Check

1. What did Benjamin's camel look like?
2. Why do you think Benjamin's father didn't take the camel's advice?
3. Do you think Benjamin really thought the camel drank up all the water? Why or why not?
4. What is the most wonderful thing that you have ever imagined? Tell about it.

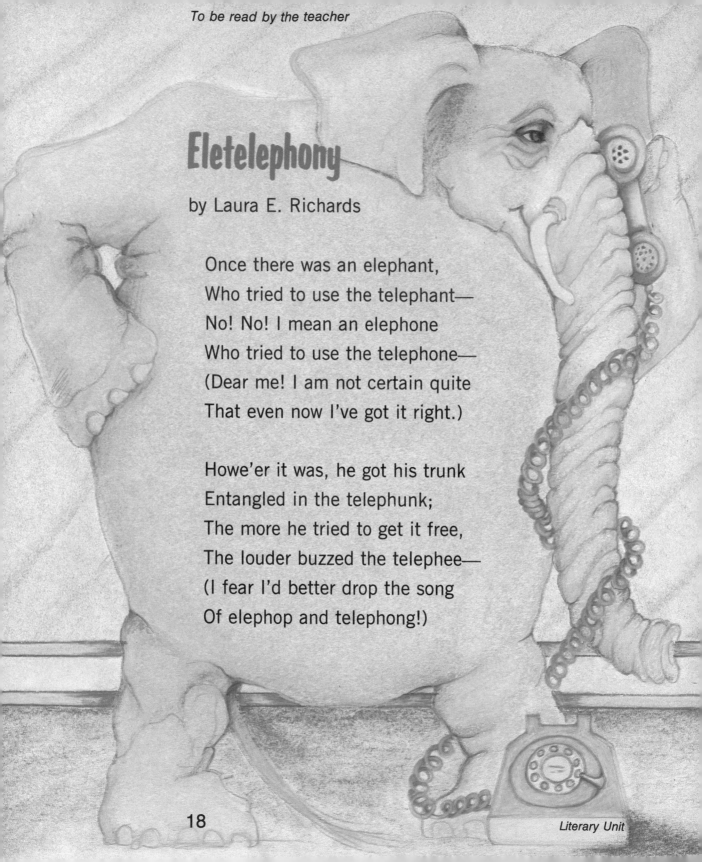

Eletelephony

by Laura E. Richards

Once there was an elephant,
Who tried to use the telephant—
No! No! I mean an elephone
Who tried to use the telephone—
(Dear me! I am not certain quite
That even now I've got it right.)

Howe'er it was, he got his trunk
Entangled in the telephunk;
The more he tried to get it free,
The louder buzzed the telephee—
(I fear I'd better drop the song
Of elephop and telephong!)

18

Have You Seen a Bat?

Many words have more than one meaning. To understand these words, you must see how they are used in a story.

Hi! Milt. I just came from the zoo. I saw a strange bat flying around in a cave.

Helene, the only bat I know is the one you use to play baseball.

Well, Milt, this bat is an animal. It looks like a flying mouse. You can't play baseball with it!

In the cartoon, the word <u>bat</u> has two meanings. You can understand each meaning when you read how the word is used in a sentence.

1. What did the word <u>bat</u> mean to Helene?
2. What did <u>bat</u> mean to Milt?
3. What should you do to understand which meaning of a word is meant in a sentence?

Practice

Read the paragraphs below. Find the word that has more than one meaning.

Winter is over. Today is the first day of spring. It is warm outside, and the flowers are blooming.

Alan was so excited, he jumped up and down on his bed. Then suddenly, he heard a loud <u>boing</u>! Something had popped out of his bed.

"Oh, no!" he cried. "I just broke a spring!"

1. In the first example, what does the word spring mean?
   a. a time of year
   b. a piece of metal that goes around and around
2. What does the word spring mean in the second example?
   a. a time of year
   b. a piece of metal that goes around and around

Some words in the next story, "Mr. Egbert Nosh," may have two meanings. Read the sentences carefully in order to figure out the correct meaning of the words.

Mr. Egbert Nosh

by Paul Groves

Once upon a time there was a man called
Egbert Nosh. *Mr. Egbert Nosh!* Mr. Egbert Nosh
lived in a house. His house was on a pretty
street. It looked just like the other houses.
But Egbert liked his house best. It was strong
and it had a beautiful, blue door. All around
it were green bushes. Egbert loved coming home
to his own house. That is, until one day when
Egbert Nosh went out for a walk.

Suddenly, he heard footsteps behind him.
VERY HEAVY FOOTSTEPS. Egbert looked back to
see who was following him. What do you think
he saw?

His house was walking down the sidewalk.

"Stop!" Egbert shouted. "This is silly."

"Why?" asked the House.

"Houses can't walk," said Egbert.

"I can," explained the House, moving right beside him. "I want to come with you. I am lonely."

"You can't come with me. You're a house. You're not a dog. Go home, House," said Egbert.

"No. Not until you do," the House said.

"I'm not going back!" cried Egbert.

"Then I'm not either," answered the House.

"This is silly!" said Egbert.

Egbert felt silly standing in the middle of the sidewalk talking to a house. What would he do if somebody saw him? So he went back home. The House followed.

When they got home, the House dusted off its shoes and sat down. Egbert opened the front door and went inside. He was very, very angry. But what could he do?

Suddenly, he had a great idea. Quietly, he opened the front door. Even more quietly, he shut it. Then he ran down the street as fast as he could.

Just around the corner was a bus stop. If he could get on a bus, he would be OK.

But what do you think he found when he got to the bus stop? Yes . . . his House.

"What are you doing here?" said Egbert.

"Waiting for a bus," said the House.

"Houses don't go on buses," Egbert said.

"I do," said the House.

Just then, a bus stopped.

"Is this your house, sir?" asked the driver.

"Yes," explained Egbert. "But it's not with me."

"Well, I'm afraid it's much too big. It can't get on the bus," the driver said.

Before Egbert could say another thing, a police
officer walked up to him.

"Is the house standing beside you yours?"
she asked.

"I'm afraid it is," answered Egbert.

"Well, sir," said the police officer, "you
can't park houses here. Take it away at once,
please."

Egbert opened the front door and went
inside. The House turned around and walked
home.

Egbert was very, very angry. How could he
make his House stay home? What could he do?
He had to go out sometime. He had to visit
friends.

Suddenly, he had an idea.

He put on an old coat and a funny hat. Then he added dark sunglasses. He found a beard he had once worn in a play. He put that on too.

Egbert was very pleased with himself. The House would never know him now. He pulled his hat down. He made sure his beard was on right. Then he ran outside.

Egbert had reached the corner when a voice said,

"It must be fun dressing up."

Yes, it was the House.

Egbert was very, very, very angry. He stormed back home. The House followed close behind.

Egbert walked into the House and pulled the door shut. He decided to go to bed. He lay down on his back. He tossed and turned and turned and tossed. But no matter how he turned and tossed, he could not fall asleep.

Then suddenly, he had another great idea. If he went out now it would be dark. The House would never be able to see him in the dark.

Quietly, Egbert opened the front door. Quietly, he shut it. On his hands and knees, he crawled away from the House. He crawled around some bushes. Then he stopped and listened. Not a sound.

He crawled some more. Then all of a sudden he heard a noise. It sounded like footsteps. He looked back through the bushes. In the dark, he could just make out HIS HOUSE!

"This is silly!" shouted Egbert.

"Shhh!" said the House. "It's late. Don't shout. You'll wake up everybody on the street."

Just then, there was another noise.

"Who's there?" asked Egbert. "There's somebody with you."

"It's me," said the Garage. "I got lonely."

"Oh, no!" cried Egbert.

Then there was another noise. A kind of clattering noise.

"There's somebody else there," said Egbert.

"It's me," said the Garbage Can. "I got lonely too."

The House, the Garage, and the Garbage Can stood on the sidewalk. The House sat down. Egbert opened the front door. He went inside. He had no more ideas.

"House," he finally said, "we must come to an agreement."

"I thought you would see it my way," said the House.

"If I take you out on Sundays, will you stop following me for the rest of the week?" Egbert said.

"May we go to the park on Sundays?" asked the House. "And may we take the Garage and the Garbage Can?"

"If we must," said Egbert.

"Great! It's a deal," the House shouted out.

So, if you ever go to call on Egbert Nosh, don't go on a Sunday. He won't be there. His House won't be there; nor will his Garage; nor his Garbage Can. But you'll know where they are, won't you?

Comprehension Check

1. Why did the house say that it was following Egbert around?
2. Why do you think Egbert put on a funny hat, sunglasses, and a beard?
3. What was the deal Egbert made with the house? Do you think it was a good deal? Why or why not?
4. What would you do if you found your house following you? Make up a story telling what you would do.

Skill Check

Egbert looked back to see who was following him.

1. In this sentence <u>back</u> means _____.

    a. behind him   b. part of a person's body

He lay down on his back.

2. In this sentence <u>back</u> means _____.

    a. behind him   b. part of a person's body

Gabrielle and Selena

by Peter Desbarats

Gabrielle and Selena went every place together. They did everything together. In fact, neither of them could remember a time when they had not been together. They were like sisters.

Gabrielle always seemed to know what Selena was thinking. Sometimes Selena knew what Gabrielle was going to say even before she said it.

One summer day, they were standing on the sidewalk. "Sometimes I wish, Selena, that I were you," said Gabrielle.

"Why do you want to be me?" asked Selena.

"I'm tired of being myself," Gabrielle said. "Every morning I wake up in the same room, and look at the same sister. I say hello to the same mother and father, and I eat the same breakfast. I'm tired of doing all these same things. I think it would be more fun to live at your house."

"But it's the same at my house," said Selena. "I always wake up in the same room and look at the same brother and eat the same breakfast and . . ."

"But you don't do them *exactly* the same," Gabrielle cut in. "It would be much more fun if I could be you and you could be me."

34

"That's silly," said Selena.

"No, it isn't—it's magic," said
Gabrielle. "All we have to do is put our
hands together, like this. Then we put our
feet together and put our noses together.
Now I'll look into your eyes, like this,
and . . ."

Selena started to laugh.

"Stop laughing or it won't work," said
Gabrielle. "Now we turn around once and I
say—'I am Selena.'"

"And I say—'I am Gabrielle,'" said
Selena.

They each took two steps back. Then they looked at each other.

"Hello, Gabrielle," said Gabrielle.

"Hello, Selena," said Selena.

"Well," said Gabrielle, "it's almost time for supper. I'd better hurry. Good-by, Gabrielle. Have fun at my house. I mean, your house."

"Good-by, Selena," said Selena. "Don't forget to feed my cat. I mean, your cat."

36

When Gabrielle reached Selena's house, she knocked at the door. Selena's mother opened it.

"Hello, Gabrielle," she said.

"I'm not Gabrielle," said Gabrielle. "I'm Selena."

"Oh, I see," said Selena's mother. "Well then, wash your hands," she said. "It's time for supper. We're having your favorite vegetable—turnips."

"Turnips are my favorite vegetable?" asked Gabrielle, who couldn't stand them.

"Sure they are," said Selena's mother. "You always have extra helpings."

"Ugh!" said Gabrielle to herself.

When Selena reached Gabrielle's house, she walked right in. She went straight to the kitchen.

"What's for supper?" she asked.

"Oh," said Gabrielle's mother, "are you staying for supper, Selena?"

"Sure," said Selena, "and my name is Gabrielle."

Gabrielle's mother turned around and looked at her.

"Where's Gabrielle? I mean, Selena?" she asked.

"Selena's at my house," said Selena. "I mean, her house."

"Very well, Gabrielle," said Gabrielle's mother. "We're having your favorite—a great big omelet."

"That's my favorite?" asked Selena.

"You always ask for extra helpings," said
Gabrielle's mother.

"Extra helpings of omelet!" said Selena
to herself. "Ugh!" She did not like omelets
at all.

Somehow Selena ate most of her supper.
Then it was time for dessert. But for Selena,
there was only bread and butter.

"Where's my dessert?" said Selena.

"Why, Gabrielle," said Gabrielle's mother,
"you always say that the best dessert is
bread and butter."

"I do?" said Selena. "Ugh!" she thought.

Gabrielle finished most of her turnip. She tried to look as if she liked it. Then Selena's father said,

"Now it's time to clear the table and wash the dishes."

"Wash the dishes?" said Gabrielle in a small voice. "But I always watch television after supper."

"I don't know what you're talking about, Selena," said Selena's mother. "You never watch television. You always say it's much more fun to wash the dishes."

At Gabrielle's house, Selena was sweeping the kitchen floor. Gabrielle's mother had said that this was what she did every night before she went to bed at seven o'clock.

"Boy!" said Selena to herself. "No wonder Gabrielle wanted to be me. Omelets. Sweeping the kitchen. No television. This is a terrible way to live."

She looked up at Gabrielle's mother.

"I'm going home," she said.

"All right, Selena," said Gabrielle's mother, laughing.

At Selena's house, Gabrielle had just finished the dishes.

"Time for bed," said Selena's father.

"But it's only seven o'clock," said Gabrielle.

"Seven o'clock!" said Selena's father. "Is it that late? Oh, dear, you must really be tired. By this time you're usually sound asleep on the back porch."

"The back porch?" said Gabrielle.

"Sure. You always say that you like sleeping outside," Selena's father said.

"Boy!" said Gabrielle to herself. "Turnips!
Washing the dishes! Sleeping on the back porch!
This is terrible!"

Then she looked up at Selena's father.

"I'm going home," she said.

"All right," said Selena's father, smiling.
"Good-by, Gabrielle."

The two girls met on the sidewalk between
Selena's house and Gabrielle's house.

"Hello, Selena," said Selena, looking at Gabrielle.

"Never mind calling me Selena," said Gabrielle. "I wouldn't be you for anything! You didn't tell me turnips were your favorite vegetable."

"Turnips?" said Selena. "I can't stand turnips. They are not my favorite vegetable. But you didn't tell me that you loved omelets."

"Ugh!" said Gabrielle. "I don't like omelets almost as much as I don't like washing dishes."

"But you sweep the kitchen floor every night," said Selena.

"I do not," said Gabrielle. "And I don't sleep on the back porch either."

44

"Who sleeps on the back porch?"cried Selena.

"But your father said . . ." said Gabrielle.

"And your mother said . . ." said Selena.

Suddenly, the two girls looked at each other and started to laugh. Their laughter sounded like singing bells beneath the trees beneath the stars beneath the still dark sky.

Comprehension Check

1. Why did Gabrielle want to change places with Selena?

2. Why do you think Gabrielle didn't like being Selena? Why do you think Selena didn't like being Gabrielle?

3. At the end of the story, why do you think the two girls are laughing? Do you think they have learned something? Tell why you think as you do.

4. Have you ever wanted to change places with a friend? Why or why not?

Skill Check

Take a look at the words below. Each appeared in the story you just read.

ate	and	wake	dark
girl	like	fun	then

1. Which words have short vowel sounds?
2. Which words have long vowel sounds?
3. Which words have r-controlled vowel sounds?

Figuring Out Words

Some sentences you read may have words you don't know. Read the story below. How did Debbie figure out the word she didn't know?

Debbie was going to her music lesson. On her way, she passed a big store. In the window she saw a sign that read "Hurry! Big holiday sale going on now!"

Debbie knew most of the words in the sign. She did not know the word holiday. First she tried to think of a word that made sense in the sentence. "What kind of sale would people have?" she asked herself.

She tried wonderful, exciting, and special. But none of these words began with the same consonant sound as the word holiday.

Then she tried happy. Happy began with the same sound but didn't make sense in the sentence.

Then Debbie remembered. During this month there were many special days. Some people called them holidays. The store would have holiday sales because some people like to buy things at that time. She looked at the word in the sign again. Sure enough, the word holiday made sense, and the consonants fit.

What steps did Debbie follow to understand the word? First she tried to think of a word that made sense in the sentence. Then she tried to see if the consonants in her word matched the consonants in the printed word.

Practice

What is the missing word in each sentence? Follow the steps that Debbie followed. Think of words that make sense in the sentence. Then match the consonants in your word with the consonants in the new word.

1. Mario went to the b__rb__r to have his hair cut.

2. Hector began his sentence with a c_p_t_l letter.

3. Leslie ate s_pp_r with her family at six o'clock.

4. Elaine made a v_s_t to her grandmother's house.

5. Harold's father put b_tt_r on his bread.

6. Gina spilled the soap p_wd_r in the sink.

Read the next story about musical instruments. Try to figure out the words that look new to you. First think of words that make sense in the sentence. Then match the consonants in your word with the consonants in the new word.

Everyday Music

by Claire Stevens

There are many different kinds of languages. Some are spoken in many countries. Others are spoken in only one or two countries. But there's one language that's spoken and understood all over the world. What is that language? It's music!

When you sing or whistle, you're speaking the language of music. When you play an instrument or clap your hands, you're speaking the language of music too.

How did this language come to be? It started thousands of years ago when people heard music in the everyday sounds around them. They heard birds singing and leaves rustling in the wind. They listened to animal noises and the rushing sound of water. They even listened to the sounds of their own heart beat. Then they tried to make all these musical sounds themselves.

How did they do this? At first, people tried to imitate everyday sounds with their own voices. But they found out that a person's voice could not imitate every sound. So they began inventing different ways to make the everyday sounds they heard.

People made instruments they could blow into, like flutes and horns. They made instruments with strings, like guitars and violins. People also made instruments they could beat, like drums and bongos.

Take a look at the following instruments. Each one makes a very different kind of musical sound.

PANPIPES

FLUTE

RECORDER

VIOLIN

TROMBONE

SAXOPHONE

TRUMPET

STAND-BASS

DRUM

CYMBALS

GUITAR

BANJO

TIMPANI

BONGOS

CELLO

LUTE

TAMBOURINE

Just like the people of long ago, you can make musical instruments too. You can make them out of simple, everyday things. Then you'll be able to imitate the sounds you hear. You'll be able to play songs you know. You may even be able to make up songs of your own.

On the next four pages you'll find directions for making three musical instruments. One is a musical instrument you blow into. It's called panpipes. The second is a string instrument. By plucking its strings, you can play different songs and rhythms. The third instrument is called a bongo drum. You can beat out all kinds of rhythms on a bongo.

All three of these musical instruments are easy to make and easy to play. Just follow the directions. Soon you'll have enough instruments to start your own everyday music band.

Making Panpipes

What you will need:

1. 3 pieces of heavy, coated construction paper. The three pieces should be different sizes. Each should be rolled into a tube and taped together.
2. clay
3. strong tape

Step One

Roll three small pieces of clay so that they will fit into the tubes.

Step Two

Put one piece of clay into each tube. If you fit it in right, the clay should close off one end of the tube.

Step Three

Place the tubes side by side. Look at the size of each piece. Put the shortest tube on one end. Put the longest tube on the other end.

54

Step Four

Put a piece of clay in between each piece
of tube.

Step Five

Tape the three pieces of tube together. When you
are finished, your panpipes should look like this:

Now you are ready to play your panpipes.
Playing panpipes is like blowing across the
top of a bottle. Put the pipes up to your mouth
and blow across them. (Don't blow into them.)

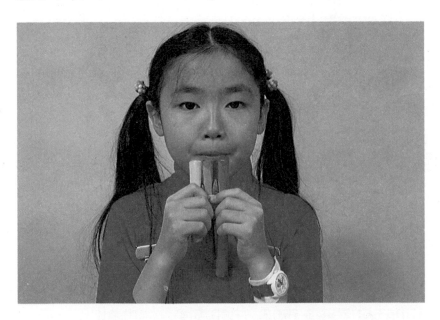

It may take a little while to get the feel
of it. Once you do, you can make all kinds of
musical sounds on the panpipes.

Making a String Instrument

What you will need:

1. a shoe box
2. 4 rubber bands of different sizes
3. 2 pencils

Step One

Make a round hole in the middle of your shoe box top. This is called a sound hole.

Step Two

Put four rubber bands all the way around the box. Each should lie across the sound hole.

Step Three

Put one pencil under the rubber bands on the left side of the box top. Put another pencil under the rubber bands on the right side.

Your string instrument is finished. Now it's time to try it out. Play the strings and see what kinds of sounds you get. First play the strings one at a time. Then play them all together. Can you hear how each rubber band makes a different sound?

Making a Bongo Drum

What you will need:

1. 2 empty tin cans. One should be bigger than the other. Each should have a plastic top.
2. strong tape
3. paint (any color you like)

Step One

Put the tin cans together so that their tops are touching. Leave the top on each can.

Step Two

Tape the two cans together.

Step Three

Paint the cans. Use the colors you like best.

Your bongo drums are all ready. The bigger can will make a low sound when you play it. The smaller can will make a higher sound.

Now beat out all kinds of different rhythms and sounds. Beat your drum along with records. Or play along with the music you hear on the radio.

Comprehension Check

1. What language is spoken and understood all over the world?
2. Of the three musical instruments you learned to make, which do you think sounds most like a heartbeat?
3. Name three steps for making a bongo drum.
4. If you could play any musical instrument, which one would you choose?

Skill Check

Read the sentence about a musical instrument. Then answer the questions that follow.

The piano is a large musical instrument that has eighty-eight keys.

a. Think of a word that makes sense in the sentence. See if the consonants in your word match the consonants in the underlined word.
b. Name a large instrument that has eighty-eight keys.
c. What is the underlined word?

Fidelia

by Ruth Adams

Fidelia Ortega was part of a musical family. Fidelia's father played the trumpet in a big band. Her brother Alberto played the trombone in the school orchestra. Her sister Carmela played the flute. She was in the school orchestra too.

Fidelia didn't play anything.

She wanted to play the violin. The violins sat right in front of the orchestra. They sang in clear, ringing voices.

"But you can't play the violin," said Alberto. "Your arms are too short. Your hands are too small."

"You are just too young," said Carmela. "Miss Toomey chooses older children to play the violin. You are only in second grade."

Fidelia decided to talk to Miss Toomey. She stopped by the music room the very next day. The orchestra was practicing. Fidelia tiptoed inside.

TOOM-ROOM-ROOM. That was Alberto's trombone.

TRA-LA-LA-LA. That was Carmela's flute. Over them all, the violins sang.

"I could play like that," Fidelia thought. She tiptoed closer to the orchestra. She could almost see herself playing the violin.

60

CRASH! BAM! BONG! Fidelia flew right into the rhythm section.

"What have we here?" Miss Toomey asked.

"It's our sister Fidelia," said Carmela.

"She wants to play in the orchestra," put in Alberto.

"What instrument do you want to play?" Miss Toomey asked Fidelia.

"Violin," whispered the girl.

"Dear me," said Miss Toomey. "You're a little too young. The violin is hard to learn, even for older children. However, we need a bongo drum player for the new song we are learning. Would you like to try?"

Fidelia looked up. "Yes," she said.

So Fidelia played the bongo drum with the orchestra. It was fun, but it wasn't the same as singing out the music on a beautiful violin. Still, Fidelia did her best. She practiced different rhythms. She learned when to play quietly. She learned when to play loudly. She learned how to tell when to stop. But she wished more than ever that she could sweep a bow across the strings of a violin.

Every week she asked Miss Toomey if she were old enough to play the violin. Every week Miss Toomey shook her head.

"Not yet, Fidelia," she would say.

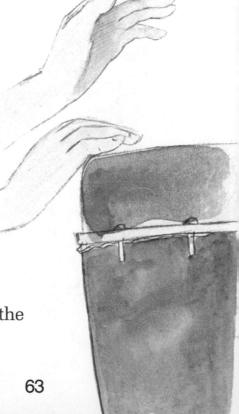

Then one morning at orchestra practice
Miss Toomey stood up.

"Boys and girls," she said. "Mrs. Reed,
the head of the All City Orchestra, is coming
next week. She will listen to you play. Then
she will choose some of you to play in the
All City Orchestra concert."

Fidelia shook her head. She beat her bongo
sadly. How would she ever get into the All
City Orchestra? If only she knew how to play
the violin!

Fidelia had an idea. On her way home
from school, she stopped at a little shop.

"Do you have an old wood box?" she asked the
woman inside.

"Well, let's see." The woman reached under a table. "Here we are. I thought there was one around somewhere."

"Oh, thank you." Fidelia hugged the box and hurried on. Now all she needed was a board.

Down the block from the Ortega house a new building was going up. Fidelia looked at some old wood sitting on the sidewalk. At last she found a board that looked about right. She picked it up. Then she rushed home.

Back home, she took her box and her board into the garage and shut the door. But before she could get to work, the garage door opened and shut again. It was Alberto.

"What are you doing?" he asked.

"I'm making something," Fidelia said shyly.

"Let me see. Come on. I won't laugh," said Alberto. He leaned over to take a look.

"What is it?" he wanted to know.

"Now it is just a box," said Fidelia. "But it is going to be a violin."

Alberto smiled. He picked up the box and looked it over.

"Here," he said. "Let me help."

Fidelia and Alberto worked together for some time. Then at last they were done. Fidelia hugged her brother.

"It's perfect!" she cried. "Thank you for helping. It is almost exactly like a real violin."

Fidelia hurried away. She had to find somewhere to practice. At last she knew the perfect place. It was just small enough for her. Fidelia walked into a little closet. She made room for herself on the floor. Then she began to practice.

By dinner time her hands hurt from practicing. Still, she didn't mind. She had learned how to imitate the sound of a violin.

Finally, the day came for Mrs. Reed to choose the players for the All City Orchestra concert. Fidelia let Carmela and Alberto start for school before her. As soon as they left, she hid her violin in a little bag.

Then she hurried out the door.

The orchestra was practicing when Fidelia
tiptoed into the room.

Quietly, she took out her homemade
violin. Quietly, she fit it under her chin.

The music of the other violins filled the
room like moonlight. Fidelia knew just how to
imitate their sounds.

BZZ . . . bzzz . . . zubb . . . zubb . . . !

Miss Toomey looked around. Suddenly
Fidelia saw that everyone else had stopped
playing. They were all looking at her too.

"Fidelia, what is this?" Miss Toomey asked.

"I made it," she said. "Alberto helped me."

Mrs. Reed held out her hand.

"May I see it?" she said. She looked at the little violin.

"Was this your own idea?" she asked.

Fidelia shook her head yes.

"It was a good idea. You and Alberto are good workers. Would you like to play a real violin?"

"Oh, yes! But I am too little. I must wait until I'm older," said Fidelia.

"Hm," said Mrs. Reed. She called to Alberto. She whispered something in his ear.

Alberto ran out the door. In two minutes
he was back. Under his arm was the smallest
violin case any of the children had ever
seen.

Mrs. Reed opened the case.

"This is a small quarter-size violin, boys
and girls. I think it will be perfect. Let's
see how it fits Fidelia."

It fit Fidelia exactly right.

As always, the musical family of Fidelia Ortega had its place in the All City Orchestra concert.

TOOM-ROOM-ROOM! That was Alberto's trombone.

TRA-LA-LA-LA! That was Carmela's flute.

This year Fidelia could only sit and watch and listen. But she didn't care. Now she had a violin exactly her size. She was in the beginning violin class. That was a start.

And everybody has to start somewhere.

Comprehension Check

1. In the beginning of the story, why didn't Miss Toomey think Fidelia could play the violin?
2. Why do you think Fidelia made a violin?
3. Do you think Fidelia showed that she was old enough to play the violin? What makes you think as you do?

To be read by the teacher

Listening to Music

by Marchette Chute

When I am hearing music
    I sometimes think of things
Like summer nights, or thunder,
    Or birds with giant wings,
Or flowers in the moonlight
    Beside a waterfall.
But mostly I sit happy
    And do not think at all.

The Surprise Party

by Annabelle Prager

"Know what?" said Nicky.

"No, what?" said Albert.

"My birthday is coming," said Nicky. "I am going to have a birthday party."

"Great!" said Albert. "Are you going to invite me?"

"Of course I'm going to invite you," said Nicky. "I'm going to invite you and Ann, and Jenny and Jan, and Morris and Doris, and Dan."

"That is a lot of people," said Albert.

"You have to have a lot of people at a birthday party," said Nicky. "That way you get a lot of gifts. Come on. I need you to help me."

72

Nicky looked in his pockets. Out came one dime, two dimes, three dimes.

"Oh, no," he said, looking very worried. "This isn't enough money for a party."

"What are you going to do?" said Albert.

"I'll think of something," said Nicky.

Suddenly his face broke into a grin.

"I know," he said. "I'll have a surprise party."

"A surprise party for who?" asked Albert.

"A surprise party for me," Nicky said.

"You can't give your own surprise party," said Albert. "You won't be surprised."

"Of course I can't give a surprise party for myself," said Nicky.

His face broke into a bigger grin.

"But you can," he said, "you and Ann, and Jenny and Jan, and Morris and Doris, and Dan."

"How are we going to do that?" asked Albert.

"Easy," said Nicky. "You say—'Listen everyone, Nicky's birthday is coming. Let's give him a surprise party.' Then they'll say— 'What a good idea. We love surprise parties.' You can bring the cake. Ann can bring the candles. Jenny can bring the . . ."

"Oh, I get it," said Albert. "Everyone will bring something for the party. What a good idea."

"You can get the party ready at my house while I'm out having my tuba lesson," Nicky said. "When I come home you will yell SURPRISE! And," he added, "I will act surprised. You know what, Albert?" he went on.

"No, what?" said Albert.

"I'll be very surprised if this doesn't turn out to be the best surprise party that ever was," Nicky said.

Albert called up Ann, and Jenny and Jan, and Morris and Doris, and Dan.

They all went to Albert's house to plan the party.

"We can fix the party at Nicky's house while he's out having his tuba lesson," said Albert. "When he comes home we will jump out and yell SURPRISE!"

Just then the telephone rang. Albert answered it.

"Hello," he said.

It was Nicky.

"I forgot to tell you something," whispered Nicky. "I love balloons with *Happy Birthday* on them."

"OK," said Albert, nervously. "Good-by."

"Who was that?" asked Ann.

Albert thought very fast.

"Uh . . . that was my Aunt Belinda," he said. "Shall we have balloons with *Happy Birthday* on them?"

"Yes, yes, yes," shouted everyone.

Ring-ring-ring.

The telephone rang again. Albert got it.

"Can we have snappers?" asked Nicky. "The kind that go pop when you pull them?"

"Sure, Aunt Belinda," said Albert. He slammed the telephone down so hard it almost broke. Then he turned to the others.

"Shall we have snappers?" he asked.

"The kind that go pop?" said Jenny. "They are so scary. I love them."

Ring-ring-ring.

The telephone rang again. Of course, Albert picked it up.

"Be sure that everyone brings a gift," said Nicky. "And remember my favorite color is blue."

"OK, Aunt Belinda. GOOD-BY!" said Albert.

"Why does your aunt call you every five minutes?" asked Morris and Doris.

"My Aunt Belinda is very lonely," said Albert. "Now let me think. Nicky's favorite color is blue. So I'll make him a blue cake."

"Do we have to bring gifts?" asked Dan.

"Everyone has to bring a gift," Albert said.

"Oh boy, will Nicky be surprised," said Jan.

The next day Nicky and Albert went skating.

"It would be awful if anyone found out that I know about the party!" said Nicky.

"Shhhh!" said Albert. "Here comes Ann now."

Nicky winked at Albert.

"Hello, Ann," he said. "Guess what I'm doing on my birthday?"

"What?" asked Ann. She gave Albert a worried look.

"My tuba teacher is taking me to a concert," said Nicky.

"Oh, no! How awful!" said Ann.

"Why do you say that?" asked Nicky. "Don't you like concerts?"

"Yes, I mean no, I mean I have to go," said Ann. She ran off as fast as she could.

Nicky laughed and laughed.

"I fooled her," he said. "Now nobody will think I know about the party. Oh, I can't wait for my birthday to come."

Three days later Nicky was walking home from his tuba lesson. He gave a little jump for joy because his birthday had finally come.

When Nicky got to his little house it was all dark. He practiced making a surprised face. He opened his front door. Nothing happened. He turned on the light. Nobody was there. There was no one to act surprised for.

"Where's the party?" Nicky wondered. He was beginning to get worried.

Then the bell rang.

"There they are!" he thought, laughing with joy. He practiced acting surprised all the way to the door.

It was Albert. He was alone.

"Where is my party?" asked Nicky.

"Oh, Nicky," said Albert. "It's awful! Ann told everyone you were going to a concert with your tuba teacher. So they called off the party."

"Oh, no!" Nicky said sadly. "My beautiful surprise party! I should never have played a trick on my friends."

"Never mind," said Albert. "I made a cake for you anyway. Come to my house and we can eat it."

They walked to Albert's house. Albert opened his front door. Nicky went in. Albert turned on the light.

"SURPRISE! SURPRISE!" yelled Ann, and Jenny and Jan, and Morris and Doris, and Dan.

Nicky looked around. He saw a beautiful blue birthday cake. He saw balloons and snappers. Best of all, he saw gifts. Each gift had a big bow on it. Each one had a surprise inside.

"Oh, boy!" Nicky shouted with joy.

"Know what?" said Albert, with a grin.

"No, what?" said Nicky.

"You said you wanted the best surprise party that ever was. So we made it a surprise!"

Comprehension Check

1. Whose idea was the surprise party?
2. Why do you think Nicky told Ann he was going to a concert on his birthday?
3. Do you think Albert did a good job of planning the surprise party? Why or why not?
4. How would you plan a surprise party? Tell what you would do.

Skill Check

Answer the following questions about the story you just read.

1. Why does Albert plan a surprise party for Nicky?
2. What does Nicky tell Ann when he meets her in the park?
3. What does Ann do when she learns Nicky is going to a concert?
4. Why is there no surprise party at his house when Nicky gets home?
5. Why does Albert bring Nicky to his house?
6. At the end of the story, why is Nicky really surprised?

Using a Dictionary or Glossary

Skill Lesson

Brog hurried back to his spaceship. "Grog," he said to his brother. "People here on earth say I look like a tuba. What's a tuba?"

"I don't know," said his brother.

"How can we find out?" Brog asked.

"We can use a dictionary or glossary to find the meaning of tuba," Grog said.

Words in a dictionary or glossary are in alphabetical order. To find tuba, Brog turned to a page of words beginning with t.

He found the entry for tuba. An **entry** is the word you look up and the information about the word. The first part of each entry is the **entry word.** This is the word that is explained. It is in dark print.

tub 1. a large bowl for washing clothes. 2. a bathtub. **tubs.**

tu ba a musical instrument that you play by blowing into it and pressing keys. See the picture. **tu bas.**

boy playing a tuba

The next part of an entry is the definition. The **definition** tells you what the word means. Some words have more than one definition.

Often an entry has a picture. The picture helps explain one of the definitions.

Brog read the entry for tuba.

"Say!" he exclaimed. "I like music, but I'm not a musical instrument." Then he looked at the picture.

"Besides," he said, "I don't look like a tuba. A tuba looks like ME!"

What can you learn about words from a dictionary or glossary?

Practice

1. Study the two glossary entries below.

   a. What are the two entry words?

   b. What is the first definition of the entry word <u>trunk</u>?

> **trum pet** a musical instrument that you play by blowing into it and pressing keys. See the picture. **trum pets.**
>
> **trunk** 1. the main stem of a tree. 2. an elephant's nose. 3. a big box for carrying clothes. See the picture. **trunks.**

2. There is a glossary in the back of this book. Find the entry word <u>shade</u> on page 314.

   a. Does <u>shade</u> have more than one definition?

   b. What are the definitions of <u>shade</u>?

   c. Which definition of the entry word <u>shade</u> is shown in the picture?

Read the next story about a zookeeper. You may see words you don't know. Use the glossary at the back of this book to find their meanings.

Monica Sandler is a reporter. She was sent to the Bronx Zoo and brought back this story.

A Report from the Zoo

by Monica Sandler

At ten o'clock the doors open. Parents, grandparents, and children of all ages hurry through the gates. For them, a day at the Bronx Zoo has just started. But for zookeeper Jean Ehret, the day began long before. Her day always starts at seven or eight o'clock in the morning.

The Bronx Zoo is in New York City. It's one of the largest zoos in the country. Jean is a zookeeper in the birdhouse.

I went to the zoo one day to find out about Jean and about her job. The first thing I asked was why she decided to become a zookeeper.

88

"I didn't really decide to become a zookeeper," Jean told me. "When I started working at the zoo, it was just a hobby. It was a part-time job. Then I looked for a full-time job. Since animals and birds were always important to me, the zoo was a perfect place to work fulltime."

Working at the zoo *has* been perfect for Jean. Learning about birds used to be just a hobby. Now it's her hobby *and* her job.

What does being a zookeeper in the
birdhouse mean? Jean says it means everything
from cleaning the bird exhibits to helping the
baby birds get born. It means feeding the
birds. It even means making nests for them.

"Making nests for the birds is very
important," Jean explained. "Nests help the
birds feel at home in the zoo."

Jean went on to say that birds at the
Bronx Zoo don't live in cages. They live in
settings. A *setting* is a space that looks
like the birds' real home.

90

Zookeepers learn what makes each kind of bird feel comfortable. Some birds need to be kept very warm. Others need cool places to live. Others need to have trees with lots of branches. Still others need water to swim in. The zookeepers make sure that each bird is placed in exactly the right setting.

I asked Jean what she likes most about being a zookeeper.

"Well," she explained, "the best part for me is helping to raise the baby birds. We take care of them before they are born, while they are still in their eggs. Then we help to bring them into the world."

Jean went on to explain how she raises the baby birds.

At certain times of the year, birds lay eggs. Jean and the other zookeepers collect these eggs. The eggs they collect are put into incubators. An *incubator* is a special kind of box. It keeps eggs warm until they are ready to hatch. Incubators can hold many eggs at a time.

Jean looks at the eggs in the incubators every day. Just before an egg is ready to open, Jean takes it out of the incubator. She puts it in another box called a *brooder*. The brooder also keeps the eggs warm. But the brooder is a better place for the baby bird to be born. In a brooder the bird will have room to walk around.

Did you know that in the brooder birds talk to each other even before they're born?

I didn't, until Jean told me about it. She explained that in the brooder two eggs are placed very close together. Soon a bird in one egg will begin to chirp. The bird in the other egg hears this sound. Then it begins to chirp too. All this chirping is going on while the birds are still in their eggs.

What are they chirping about? Jean says it's their way of telling each other it's time to be born.

When the baby birds first hatch, Jean feeds them every hour. She knows exactly what each bird must eat. Some feed on pieces of meat. Others feed on fish. Some even feed on dog food.

When the birds get old enough, they are put into one of the exhibits. There they share a space with other birds.

I guess you think Jean plays with the birds all the time. This is what I thought. But that's not the case. Jean says it's kinder to leave the birds alone. Birds are happier playing with other birds.

94

Besides, being a zookeeper doesn't leave much time to play with the birds. Zookeeping is hard work. Jean is always on the move. She carries heavy pails. She hoses down the exhibits. She even picks up some of the really big birds. A zookeeper has to be strong.

"I'm glad that I have always exercised," Jean told me. "I play a lot of sports. I also like camping. I've been going camping with my family since I was a little girl. All this exercise has made me strong. It has helped me with my work. But don't think my job is only hard work," Jean added. "Sometimes very funny things happen."

Jean went on to tell this story.

"One day a zookeeper brought his pet parrot
to work with him. He left the parrot at the
ostrich house. He planned to pick it up at the
end of the day. I was working at the ostrich
house that afternoon. It was very hot. I went
into the kitchen to get a drink of water. As
I began to drink, I heard a voice behind me.

"'Hey you, get back to work,' it said.

"I turned around. No one was there. I went
back to drinking my glass of water. But then
I heard the same voice again.

"'Hurry up! Get back to work,' it said.

"Now I was getting angry. I turned around
as fast as I could. What do you think I saw?
Yes, it was the other zookeeper's pet parrot.
I began to laugh. I think the bird did too."

When we were finished talking, Jean walked me outside. I thanked her for explaining about her job.

"I love my job," she said. "It's not a job for everybody. But it's perfect for me!"

Comprehension Check

1. What does Jean Ehret like best about being a zookeeper at the birdhouse?

2. Why do you think Jean says birds are happier being with other birds?

3. You read about some of Jean's hobbies and special interests. After reading about them, do you think that Jean chose a job that was right for her? Why or why not?

4. If you were a zookeeper, which animals would you want to take care of? Explain why.

Skill Check

Read these questions. Then turn to the glossary in the back of your book to find the answers.

1. On what page is the entry for *ostrich*? What is its definition?

2. Find the entry for *parrot*. Is there a picture in this entry?

3. How many definitions are there for the entry word *brooder*? Which one explains how the word was used on page 92?

Kid Dynobite

adapted from a book by Madeline Sunshine

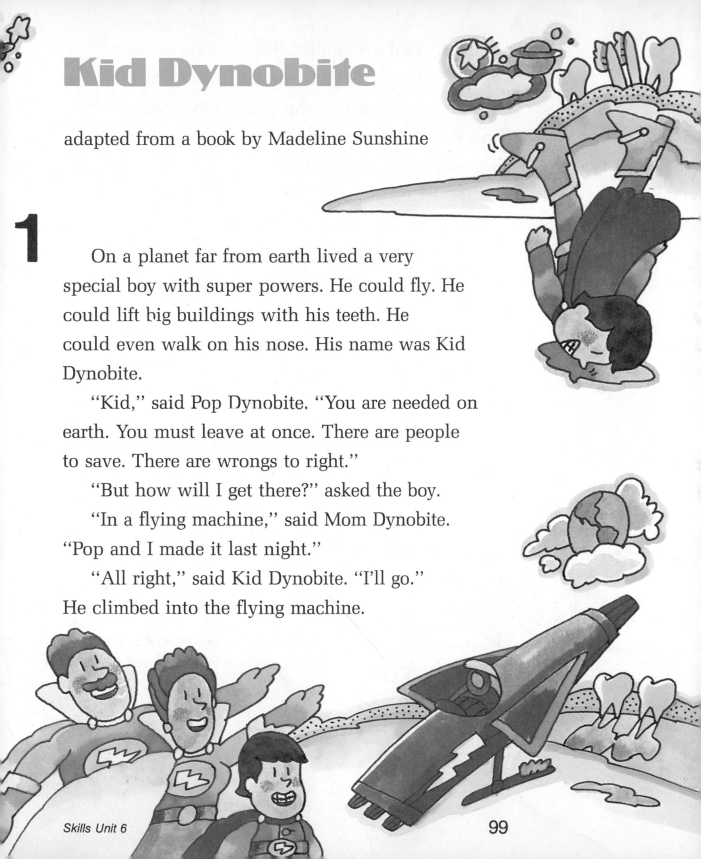

1

On a planet far from earth lived a very special boy with super powers. He could fly. He could lift big buildings with his teeth. He could even walk on his nose. His name was Kid Dynobite.

"Kid," said Pop Dynobite. "You are needed on earth. You must leave at once. There are people to save. There are wrongs to right."

"But how will I get there?" asked the boy.

"In a flying machine," said Mom Dynobite. "Pop and I made it last night."

"All right," said Kid Dynobite. "I'll go." He climbed into the flying machine.

"Kid," said his mother. "Remember, all your super powers are in your super braces. To use your powers on earth, snap your teeth together three times. And," she added, "stay away from gum—even if it's sugarless!"

"But why?" asked Kid Dynobite. "What's gum?"

There was no time for his mother to answer, for at that very moment the take-off began. Five . . . four . . . three . . . two . . .

"Wait!" screamed Kid Dynobite. "I don't know how to fly this thing!"

But it was too late. He was already shooting through the sky.

WILL THE KID GET TO EARTH SAFELY?

WILL HE BE ABLE TO STAY AWAY FROM GUM—
EVEN SUGARLESS GUM?

READ ON TO FIND OUT.

2 Kid Dynobite *did* get to earth safely. He climbed out of the flying machine. It was early morning. He looked around. A strange earth creature was headed toward him. Kid Dynobite was getting scared. He began to snap his teeth together. But before he could finish, his braces locked.

"Oh, no!" he said to himself. "Now I can't snap three times! What am I going to do?"

The earth creature was getting closer and closer.

"Say!" yelled a voice. "What are you doing? This road is for cars only."

"Of course," thought Kid Dynobite. "That's not a creature. It's a car!"

"Are you all right?" asked the woman.

Kid Dynobite could not answer.

"Look, Harry," the woman said. "His braces have locked. That's why he can't speak."

Kid Dynobite was in luck. Harry was a dentist. He fixed the Kid's braces in no time.

And that's how it happened. Harry, Martha, and Kid Dynobite became a family. They gave him a new name—Elroy Apple.

WILL ELROY FIND HAPPINESS WITH THE APPLE FAMILY?

WILL HE RIGHT WRONGS AND SAVE PEOPLE?

READ ON TO FIND OUT.

102

3   Harry and Martha took Elroy to school. But Elroy's school days were no fun. He tried to make friends. He tried to save people. But no one needed saving. The other children laughed at him.

"Look at the size of those braces!" yelled one boy.

"Yeah, just look at them," yelled another.

Elroy was feeling really sad. But then he heard one of the boys say, "The fair is in town. Let's all go!"

"What's a fair?" asked Elroy.

"It's a place where you play games and win prizes," explained a boy named Paul. "And it has scary rides that fly through the air."

"Scary rides!" thought Elroy. And that's what made up his mind. He was going to the fair.

As the boys walked to the fair, Elroy saw Paul put something into his mouth.

"What's that?" he asked.

"Here, have some," said Paul. "It's good."

Elroy took a piece.

"Chew it," said Paul. "You have to chew it."

Elroy bit down and began to chew. "It is good," he said. "What is it called?"

"Don't you know!" said Paul. "It's gum— sugarless gum."

"Gum!" shouted Elroy. "Oh, no!"

WHAT WILL THE CHEWING GUM DO TO ELROY?

WHAT WILL ELROY DO TO THE CHEWING GUM?

READ ON TO FIND OUT.

4 "Hurry, Elroy," said Paul. "We want to go on the cable cars."

Elroy didn't answer.

"What's the matter?" said another boy. "Are you scared or something?"

"Forget it," said a third boy. "We're going without you." They left and got on the ride.

Elroy was all alone. Then suddenly he heard loud screams. The cable holding up the cable cars was breaking. Children were trapped in the air.

"People in danger!" Elroy thought. "This is a job for KID DYNOBITE! But what can I do? My braces are locked!"

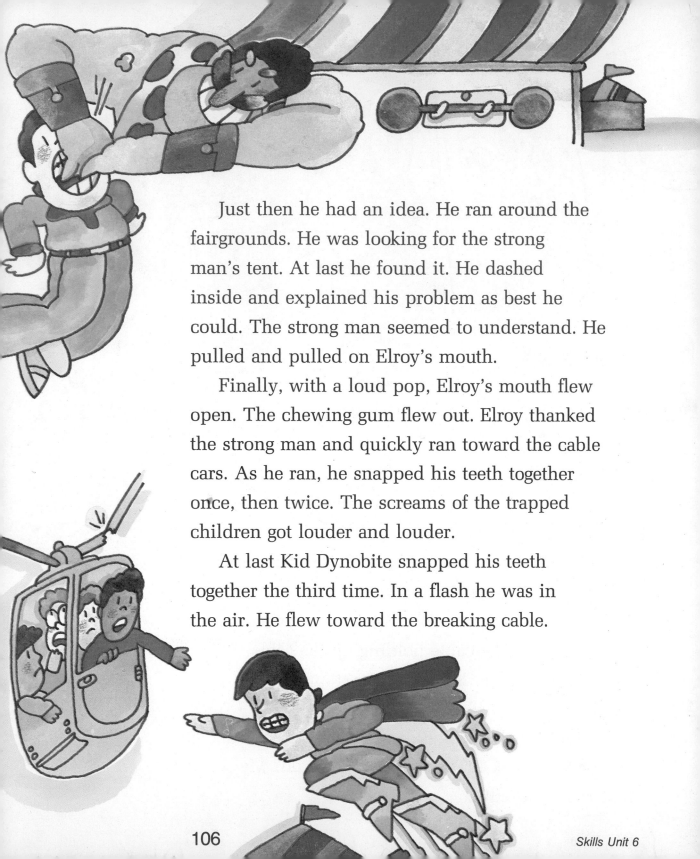

Just then he had an idea. He ran around the fairgrounds. He was looking for the strong man's tent. At last he found it. He dashed inside and explained his problem as best he could. The strong man seemed to understand. He pulled and pulled on Elroy's mouth.

Finally, with a loud pop, Elroy's mouth flew open. The chewing gum flew out. Elroy thanked the strong man and quickly ran toward the cable cars. As he ran, he snapped his teeth together once, then twice. The screams of the trapped children got louder and louder.

At last Kid Dynobite snapped his teeth together the third time. In a flash he was in the air. He flew toward the breaking cable.

"Look!" yelled a man. "Up in the sky! It's a bird! It's a plane! It's a boy with braces!"

"Yes," said a woman. "And he's wearing a strange T-shirt. It says, 'I save people. I turn wrongs to right. I'm the one, the only, KID DYNOBITE!'"

Meanwhile, Kid Dynobite reached the breaking cable. As he did, it began to snap. He grabbed both ends with his teeth. A man below started the cable cars again. Slowly they began to move.

In a few minutes each car had reached the ground. Everyone got down safely. Then, his work done, Kid Dynobite flew off. Soon he joined the other boys.

"Where have you been?" asked Paul. "You missed everything!"

"That's right," said another boy. "We almost got hurt."

"But," added Paul, "we were saved by Kid Dynobite."

"Kid Dynobite?" said Elroy, trying not to smile.

"Yes," said Paul. "He's a boy, just like us. But he has these super braces."

"You know," said a third boy. "I wish I had braces like that."

Elroy didn't say a word. He just looked at the others and smiled.

WILL ELROY EVER LET ON THAT HE IS
REALLY KID DYNOBITE?

WILL THE OTHER CHILDREN GET BRACES?

WHAT DO YOU THINK?

Comprehension Check

1. Why did Kid Dynobite's parents want him to go to earth?

2. Why was Elroy helpless when his braces were locked?

3. Do you think Kid Dynobite did all the things he set out to do on earth? Why or why not?

4. If you had super powers, what would they be? What kinds of things would you be able to do?

Skill Check

The next few sentences are from the story you just read. Read them. Then answer the questions below them.

"Kid," said Pop Dynobite. "You are needed on earth."

"But how will I get there?" asked the boy.

1. In the second paragraph, what does the word *there* stand for?

Elroy's school days were no fun. He tried to make friends. He tried to save people.

2. In sentences two and three, whom does the word *he* stand for?

Mrs. Ling's Cat

by Clyde Robert Bulla

Johnny's father worked in the city. One night he came home from work feeling very tired. He sat down on a big, soft chair. Then he said,

"Mrs. Ling called to me as I went by her house today."

"The woman who lives alone in the big house?" asked Mother.

"Yes," said Father. "She has lost her cat. She asked me if I had seen it."

He asked Johnny, "Have you seen Mrs. Ling's cat?" Then he asked Johnny's older brother the same question.

"I did see it once," said Johnny's older brother. "It has a funny face and a long, long tail. It is not a pretty cat."

"It's pretty to Mrs. Ling," Father said. "She loves her cat, and it has been gone for two days. If you see it, take it home to her."

"I'll go look for it tomorrow," said Johnny. "May I go look?"

His father smiled. "Yes," he said.

All the time he was eating supper, Johnny thought about looking for Mrs. Ling's cat. By bedtime, he had a plan.

The next day he went to the corner shop of Mr. Wu.

"Good morning, Mr. Wu," said Johnny. "Do you have any fish?"

"Yes, we have fish," said Mr. Wu. "What kind do you want to buy?"

"I don't have any money," said Johnny. "Do you have a fish you don't want anymore? An old fish you were going to throw away?"

Mr. Wu shook his head in surprise.

"Why do you want an old fish?" he asked.

"I want to find a cat with it," said Johnny.

Mr. Wu shook his head again. He went through a door into the back room. He came out with a silver pail.

"Here," said Mr. Wu. "There is a fish in the pail. It is one I don't want anymore."

"Thank you, Mr. Wu," Johnny said, taking the silver pail. He hurried out of the shop.

Johnny began to walk down the street. An orange cat smelled the fish. The cat must have been hungry. Fast as could be, it ran over and chased after Johnny and the pail. Next, a black cat smelled the fish. It was hungry too. It came running across the street after Johnny, the orange cat, and the pail. Soon, two more cats came out of an alley. Hungry for the fish, they followed along with the others.

"Come, kitty, come, kitty," called Johnny.

"Meow, meow!" cried the cats. They ran behind him.

People stopped to look at Johnny and the cats.

"See the parade," somebody shouted.

More cats were coming all the time. They got under Johnny's feet. Some of them jumped up to get to the fish. He had to put the silver pail on top of his head. Once, the fish almost fell out.

He led the cats down the street to Mrs. Ling's house.

He called, "Mrs. Ling! Mrs. Ling!"

Mrs. Ling came out.

"I brought some cats," said Johnny. "Is one of them yours?"

Mrs. Ling looked through the gate at all the cats.

"Oh, no, no!" she said. "I'm afraid my cat is not here."

"Will you look again?" asked Johnny. He was sure that one of the cats would be hers.

Mrs. Ling looked at all the cats again.

"Oh, no, no!" she said. "I'm afraid my dear little Mu is not here."

Johnny felt bad. He was hot and tired. The cats were tired too. He sat down in front of the gate. So did the cats.

All at once, Mrs. Ling began to sniff.

"What is in the pail?" she asked.

"A fish," said Johnny.

"Come inside," said Mrs. Ling.

She opened the gate just wide enough for Johnny to get through. The cats were left outside.

"I do not think that is a very good fish," she said.

"It is one that Mr. Wu did not want," said Johnny. "I took it so the cats would follow me. I thought I would find your cat."

"You are a good boy to try to find my Mu. Come in, and we will have tea and cakes."

Mrs. Ling sniffed again.

"Will you take that fish away before we have our tea?" she asked.

"Sure," said Johnny. "Where shall I take it?"

"Take it to the yard and bury it," said Mrs. Ling. "You will find a shovel there."

Johnny went around the house to the back yard. He found the shovel and began digging. While he was digging, he heard a strange sound. It was like a voice from far away.

He looked behind him. He looked all around. He saw nothing that could have made the strange sound.

He went back to digging. With the shovel, he dug a hole and buried the fish.

Just then, the strange sound came again. He listened.

"Meow, meow!"

It was a cat!

He looked up in the trees. He looked under one bush. Then he looked under another.

"Oh, my!" he said.

Under the second bush was a wide, deep hole. He looked down into it. But it was so dark he could not see anything.

"Kitty, kitty, kitty," he called.

"Meow, meow!" came from down in the hole.

118

Johnny had a string in his pocket. He tied
it to the pail. Then he dropped the pail into
the hole.

Suddenly, he felt a tap at the pail. He
began to pull and pull. The pail was heavy now.

Johnny pulled the pail up out of the hole.
In it was a cat—a yellow cat with a funny
little face and a long, long tail.

"My little Mu!" cried Mrs. Ling. She picked
the cat up in her arms. It began to purr.

Mrs. Ling looked under the bush. She
looked into the hole. Then she shook her head.

"There was an old well here long ago," she said. "Now it is empty. I put boards over it. But the boards must have worn away."

"So that's how Mu fell in," said Johnny.

"That's how she fell in," said Mrs. Ling. "I will fix it so nothing will ever fall in again.

Mrs. Ling held the cat close to her.

"Thank you for finding my little Mu," she said. "Hungry, hungry kitty! I'll get you some warm milk."

They went into the house. A girl was there. Johnny was surprised. He had thought Mrs. Ling lived alone.

"This is my granddaughter," said Mrs. Ling.

Literary Unit

"My name is Laurie," said the girl. "I came to stay with my grandmother for a few weeks. And I'm glad you found Mu. I was afraid she would never come home."

They sat on the floor and had tea. Mu had two dishes of warm milk.

"It's like a party," said Laurie.

Johnny's eyes were smiling. It *was* a party, a party Johnny would never forget.

Comprehension Check

1. Where did Johnny go to get the fish?
2. Why do you think Johnny wanted to use the fish to find the cat?
3. Do you think Johnny's plan was a good one? Why or why not?
4. Have you ever helped somebody find something that was lost? Tell about it.

Cat Bath

by Aileen Fisher

She always tries
to look her best—
she washes east,
she washes west,
she washes north,
she washes south
with the washcloth
in her mouth.

And then, without
a sign of rush,
she makes her tongue
a comb and brush
to groom her fur
or, should she choose,
to smooth the velvet
of her shoes.

Gathering Details

Details are small bits of information. They help you learn more about something. To find out more details about fireflies, read the paragraph below.

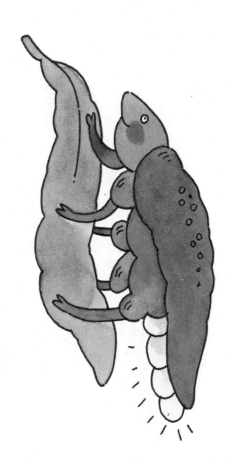

Sometimes, when it is dark outside, you can see many tiny blinking lights. They are not light bulbs. They are not stars. They are small bugs called fireflies. Fireflies blink their lights on and off to signal each other. You might say it is their way of talking. The lights are in the tails of the fireflies. Some fireflies blink faster than others.

How big are fireflies? If you said small, you picked out a detail.

Why do fireflies blink their lights on and off? If you said to signal each other, you were right. You picked out another detail. What other details about fireflies did you find in the paragraph?

Practice

Look for the details about Fluffy in this story. Then answer the questions that follow.

Susan was sad. Her dog, Fluffy, was missing. Fluffy was a large brown and white mutt. He had brown eyes and a long tail. One day Susan went to the store. On her way in, she saw a sign. It said "Found: large black and white mutt with blue eyes and long tail. Call John."

1. What does Fluffy look like?
2. What does the dog that John found look like?
3. Do you think Susan's dog is the same one John found? Why or why not?

Read the next story. Pay attention to the details to learn more about masks.

Looking at Masks

by Steve Harvey

Have you ever wanted to put on a new face? You can, you know. People have been putting on new faces for hundreds and hundreds of years. How? They have been using masks.

People have been wearing masks since early times. How do we know this? Pictures on cave walls tell us so. They show that people wore masks that were made to look like animals. The people wore these masks when they hunted. They wanted the animals to think *they* were animals too. They hoped this would help them catch the animals they were chasing.

Masks were also used in special ceremonies. Some people thought that wearing masks would chase scary things away. Beneath their masks, these people may have been afraid. But the masks they wore made them look and feel brave.

Some people even wore masks to welcome in the four seasons. They made different kinds of masks for winter, spring, summer, and fall.

People always thought of masks as a kind of magic. Masks gave people joy. There was joy in making them and joy in wearing them.

People made masks out of many different things. Some masks were faces cut out of wood. Others were made of gold and colored rocks.

126

Later on, masks were used in the theater. People acting in plays would wear them. These masks were made to show different feelings. Some had scary faces painted on them. Some were painted to look happy, sad, or angry.

But even in the theater, masks were not just for show. They had other jobs to do. Many theaters were enormous. It was hard to see the faces of the people acting. But masks were large. They could be seen, even from far away.

Some theater masks were made to help people hear the words being spoken. Special tubes were placed beneath the masks. The people acting spoke into these tubes. This helped their voices carry all around the theater.

People wore masks at parties too. Sometimes games were played. The idea of these games was to guess which person's face was beneath each mask. Prizes were handed out for the best-looking masks.

Today masks are still worn in the theater. They are also worn at costume parties. Many of these costume parties take place on New Year's Eve. You can see all different kinds of masks at that time of year.

Take a look at the masks above. Which ones would you choose to wear to a costume party? Which ones might you see in the theater?

Skills Unit 7

Some people *collect* masks as a hobby. Some people *make* masks as a hobby.

Many masks can be found in special shops. But you can make one of your own. Follow the directions on the next page. Soon you'll have a new face to play with. Then, who knows? Maybe mask making and mask collecting will become a hobby for you.

Making a Hand-Held Mask

What you will need:

1. a white paper plate
2. tape
3. 4 pieces of paper
4. paints
5. a pencil

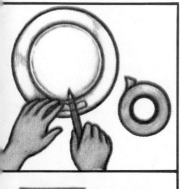

Step One

Tape the pencil to the paper plate. Put the plate aside.

Step Two

Cut each of the 4 pieces of paper in half. Cut from one corner to the opposite corner, across the middle of the paper. When you're done you'll have 8 pieces of paper.

Step Three

Starting at the corner, roll each piece of paper into a tube. Tape each tube so that it stays together.

Step Four

Tape the tubes around the paper plate. Space them out.

Step Five

Using bright colors, paint a face on the paper plate.

Now that your mask is done, try it on. How does it feel to be wearing a different face?

Comprehension Check

1. How do we know that people of long ago wore masks?
2. Why do you think wearing masks gave people joy?
3. What are the parts of your hand-held mask?
4. Have you ever worn a mask? Tell what the mask looked like.

Skill Check

Which of the following detail sentences would fit into the story you just read about masks?

1. Some masks are made out of paper bags.
2. In the winter, some people wear earmuffs.
3. Some masks only cover a person's eyes.
4. At parties some people like to dance.

Kate's Swimming Pool

adapted from a story by
Barbara Owen Webb

Kate sat on the front steps of her house. She watched the birds fly from tree to tree. She listened as they whistled to each other. One bird flew up right beside her.

"Hello, pretty bird," Kate whispered.

The bird whistled something soft and sweet. It sounded like "Hello, Kate." Then it flew away.

Kate grinned happily. She looked all around. As she did, she saw a bird splashing in a rain-water puddle.

Just then a green truck bounced up. It stopped beside the puddle.

132

Two workers got out of the truck. One had
a shovel. He used his shovel to splash water
out of the hole. The other worker had a pail
of tar. He put some tar into the hole. Then
the first worker used the back of his shovel
to smooth the tar down. The tar was still
soft so it was easy to do.

For a while Kate watched them quietly.
Then suddenly she bounced up.

"Stop!" she yelled. "You filled up the
bird's swimming pool!"

The worker with the shovel shook his head.
"It had to be filled up," he said. "Holes in
the middle of the street can be dangerous. We
filled it up so no one would get hurt."

"Don't be sad," the other worker added. "The birds will be all right. Besides, you can always make a place for the birds to swim in your yard."

With that, the two workers tossed their tools and the pail of tar into the truck. They said good-by to Kate. Then they rode away.

Kate hurried up to her house. She turned the knob on the door and went inside. Then she told her mother and father all about the two men, the birds, and the puddle.

"What you need is a birdbath like the one Grandmother has," said Kate's father. "But we can't spend money on a swimming pool for birds."

134

Kate felt really sad. She wished she had money of her own. If she had, she would buy the birdbath herself. But without money. . . .

"Wait a minute," she thought. "That worker said I should *make* a place for the birds to swim. And that's exactly what I *will* do!"

She sat down to think it out more clearly. She decided to go to the library the very next day. She'd look for a book about birdbaths. She'd make one just like her grandmother's.

At ten o'clock the following morning, Kate and her brother set out for the library. As they walked, they saw a building behind a silver gate.

"Look," said Jordy. "They are taking the building down."

Kate and Jordy watched for a while. Then Kate grabbed Jordy's arm and off they went.

At last they reached the library. They found three books about birds. Each had many pictures of birdbaths.

As they looked through the books, Kate's face broke into a grin.

"A garbage-can top!" Kate said to Jordy. She showed him a picture. "See?" she said. "That birdbath is just a garbage-can top stuck into the ground. I can make that."

She turned a few more pages.

136

Suddenly Kate began to grin from ear to ear.

"That's it, Jordy!" she cried. "That's the birdbath I'm going to make. It looks almost exactly like the one Grandmother has."

Jordy shook his head. "Forget it, Kate," he broke in. "It's a garbage-can top sitting on a big piece of pipe. We don't have a pipe. So," he went on, "let's just forget it and go home."

"We may not have a pipe now," Kate bounced back. "But we'll have one soon. Come on."

Together they left the library. They went running down the street.

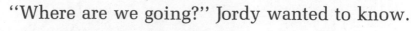

"Where are we going?" Jordy wanted to know.

"You'll see," Kate shouted.

Soon they were back beside the silver gate they had stopped at before. As they ran up to it, a whistle began blowing. It was time for the workers to have lunch.

Kate looked through the gate. She saw piles of wood, old windows, and doors with their knobs torn off. Best of all, she saw lots of pipes.

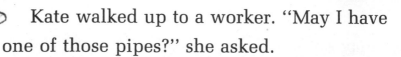

Kate walked up to a worker. "May I have one of those pipes?" she asked.

"I don't see why not," said the worker. The worker smiled as she walked over to the pile.

The worker looked at the pile of pipes. Finally she grabbed a big fat one.

"This should do it," she said, handing the pipe to Kate.

"Thank you," said the girl. Then she and Jordy hurried off.

Now all Kate needed was something to put on top of the pipe. It had to be big enough to hold water for the birds to swim in.

Kate thought for a moment.

"I know," she told her brother. "We'll go visit Dad at Buddy's Garage. I'm sure we'll find something we can use there."

Soon she and Jordy reached the garage. Their father was working on a car. They sat and watched for a while.

Then Kate spotted something shiny. It was hiding in a corner of the room.

"That's it!" she said to herself. Then she turned to her father.

"Please, Dad, can I have that shiny thing?"

"Sure. But what do you want it for?" her father asked.

"You'll see when you get home," Kate answered. Then she grabbed her brother's arm.

"Let's go, Jordy!" she shouted. She broke into a run, pulling her brother right along.

Kate's father got home at six o'clock. He rang the bell. No one answered. Then he turned the knob on the door and went into the house. He walked down the hall to the living room. No one was there.

"We're all in the yard, Dad," Kate shouted.

Her father hurried outside. There, in the middle of the yard, was a birdbath. Two birds were splashing in the water and whistling sweet songs.

Kate's father shook his head in surprise.

"Kate," he said, "you are something else! That's the best-looking birdbath I've ever seen!"

Kate smiled so hard it almost hurt. She looked at the birds swimming in the water.

"Maybe someday I can make us a swimming pool too," she said.

Everyone laughed.

"Knowing you," her mother said with a smile, "you probably will!"

Comprehension Check

1. Why do you think Kate wanted to build the birdbath?

2. What did she use to build the birdbath?

3. Do you think Kate's trip to the library was a good idea? Why or why not?

4. Have you ever made something out of simple everyday things? Tell about it.

Skill Check

1. What was Kate's problem?

2. How did she solve the problem?

3. Do you think Kate did a good job of solving her problem? Why do you think as you do?

4. Do you think Kate is the kind of person who gives up easily? Why do you think as you do?

Feelings in Stories

A story often tells how a person feels. What the person says and does show how that person feels. Other words in the story may also tell how the person feels.

Mina was angry. The new baby was crying and Mina could not sleep. Mina frowned as she looked at the baby.

"I'm mad at you," she said. "I wish you would stop crying."

Suddenly the baby stopped crying. Mina felt better, and she began to smile. "Well, I'm glad you stopped crying. Maybe you're not so bad after all," she said.

1. What word in the story tells you how Mina felt when the baby was crying?

2. What did Mina say and do that showed how she felt?

3. What word in the story tells you how Mina felt when the baby stopped crying? What did Mina say and do that showed how she felt?

Practice

Read the paragraph below. Find the words that tell you how Kathy feels. Also look for what Kathy says and does to show her feelings.

Kathy was sad. She wanted to be a clown but everyone told her she was too young. "I'm unhappy," she pouted. One day she had an idea. She got some orange hair, a funny hat, and a big red nose. Then she painted her face to look very happy. When she finished, she looked in the mirror. She began to laugh. "Look at me now," she said. "I'm a happy clown."

1. How did Kathy feel in the beginning of the story? What word tells you how she felt?
2. What did Kathy say and do that tells how she felt?
3. How did Kathy feel at the end of the story?
4. What did Kathy do that tells you how she felt?

In the next story, "Grandpa, Me, and Our House in the Tree," look for words that describe the way Nico feels.

Grandpa, Me, and Our House in the Tree

by Barbara Kirk

My name is Nico.

Today my grandfather is coming to visit me.
Grandpa and I are a perfect match. He likes
to do all the things I like to do. That's
what makes his visits extra special.

Grandpa plays the flute. It makes a sweet
sound. Sometimes I try to imitate the sounds
he makes with my voice. Someday I will take
flute lessons. Then Grandpa and I will play
our flutes together.

Grandpa and I love to run and play ball.
The two of us even built a tree house.

When Grandpa last visited, my mom took
these pictures of Grandpa and me.

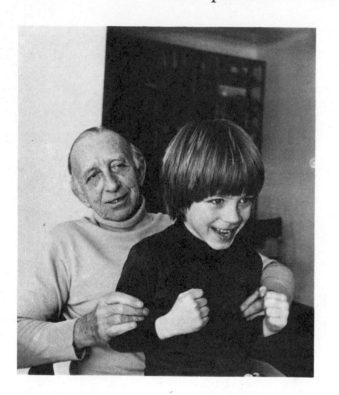 

We start to get ready for Grandpa's visit.
When Mom leaves to pick him up, Dad and I
make up the bed. Dad isn't smiling. Suddenly
he sits down and says, "Grandpa has been very
sick. It's hard for him to walk or talk. You,
Mom, and I will have to be extra helpful to him
this visit."

"I don't believe it!" I tell Dad.

I remember that Grandpa is big and strong. He was the first one to climb my tree. He even climbed up carrying wood. He hammered the longest nails in our tree house. He couldn't be sick now. I feel a knot growing inside of me. It can't be true about Grandpa being sick. It just can't be true.

But if it is true, what are we going to do? Will we still have fun together? Will Grandpa still help me with my school lessons? Will we climb up to the top of the tree house together? Will we do everyday things like play with my dog Hudson? Will Grandpa and I still share secrets? Will we still be a perfect match?

At last Grandpa is here! He looks very white and tired. He smiles only a little.

"Hi, little Nico," he says quietly.

Hudson runs over. But when Grandpa doesn't play with him, he looks sad and crawls away.

Dad puts one hand under Grandpa's arm. Then they slowly walk in the direction of the house.

I watch as Grandpa and Dad walk away. I still feel the knot inside of me. I don't know what to do. I haven't spoken to Mom about it. But I can tell that our feelings match. She's worried about Grandpa too.

When I go into his room, Grandpa just closes his eyes. He doesn't say anything. Everything seems so different. I curl up in a corner of the room. Grandpa and I have not spoken. Still, I think he knows I'm here.

Soon I feel very alone. I walk outside and go off by myself. I don't even know what direction to walk in. I just walk.

Later Mom asks me to bring Grandpa his supper. I bring the food in on a tray. I try to make sure everything is just the way Grandpa likes it.

He sits up and takes my hand.

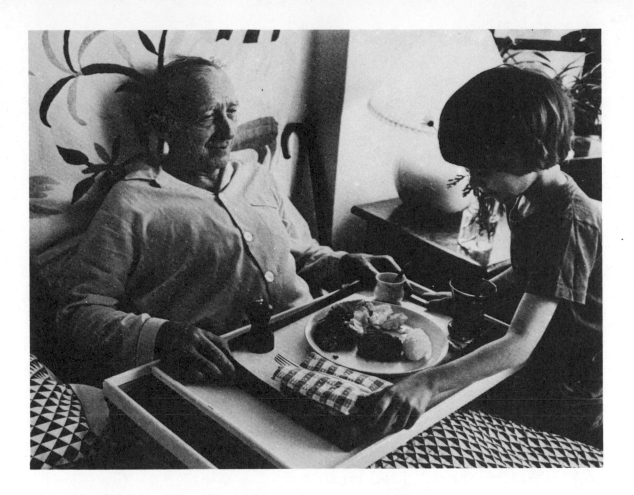

"Hi, Nico," he says. "Have you made any changes in our tree house? Do you still climb up and play there every afternoon?"

"Oh, Grandpa, you know I've been waiting for you to come and help me."

He smiles for a long time. Then he says, "You must be the big builder now. I can't climb up, but I can still help you. I'll give the directions. You carry them out. It will be fun."

Grandpa looks at me for a moment. Then he says, "By the way, do you need a telephone in the tree house?"

"A telephone? There's no telephone out there," I tell him.

"I know," Grandpa says. "But we can make one. We can make matching telephones from two cans and a piece of string. Then we can always talk to each other—even if you're high up in the tree house and I'm down on the ground. Save the next two cans of dog food you open for Hudson. Then we can put together our own special telephones."

I crawl up on Grandpa's bed and give him a hug.

150

I feed Hudson an extra can of dog food. Now I have the two cans we need to make our telephone.

But the next day, and for many days after, Grandpa stays in bed. He still has to rest. Meanwhile, I paint the cans. I paint his blue and I paint mine white. The two colors are a perfect match, just like me and Grandpa.

Many weeks later, after all the leaves have fallen off the trees, Grandpa says, "I'm feeling better now. Let's go out and put up our telephone."

I am so happy, I feel like singing. Grandpa and I walk outside and get to work.

Grandpa helps me hammer a nail into each can to make a hole. I put the ends of a long string through the holes. Grandpa ties a knot inside one can. I tie a knot inside the other. We test the knots to make sure they are strong. The knots are tied exactly right. Finally it's ready.

I climb the tree with my end of the telephone. Grandpa waits close by. Our secret code word is Mississippi. I start, "Missis—"

"—sippi," Grandpa finishes. Mississippi! It comes across loud and clear. What a match we are, my Grandpa and I!

Soon Mom comes outside. She takes this picture of Grandpa, me, and our house in the tree.

152

Comprehension Check

1. Why were Grandpa's visits so special to Nico?

2. Why do you think Nico couldn't believe that his grandfather was sick?

3. Do you think Nico showed his grandfather how much he cared about him? Why do you think as you do?

Skill Check

1. How does Nico feel about his grandfather? What does Nico say or do to tell you how he feels?

2. How does Nico feel when he learns that his grandfather is sick? What does Nico say or do to tell you how he feels?

3. What do Nico's actions toward his grandfather tell you about Nico?

4. How does Nico feel when his grandfather is well enough to help him build the telephone? What does Nico say or do to tell you how he feels?

Giants Are Very Brave People

by Florence Parry Heide

Everybody's afraid of something. But Bigelow was afraid of almost EVERYTHING!

He was afraid of clouds.

"They might fall on me," he said.

He was afraid of alphabet soup.

"What if I ate letters that spelled a magic word that would turn me into a mushroom?" he asked.

He was afraid of the rain. So he carried a big red umbrella everywhere, even on sunny days.

One day Bigelow was out walking. He was so busy looking up at the clouds that he didn't look where he was going. The first thing he knew he heard someone yelling.

Bigelow looked down. He saw a little lady running around. Bigelow had never seen such a little lady.

"Go away, go away!" screamed the lady.

"But why?" asked Bigelow.

"Because you're a giant, that's why!" the lady said.

"I am?" asked Bigelow in surprise. "I didn't think I was a giant. I just thought you were very small."

The lady peered up at Bigelow. "You didn't know you were a giant?" she asked.

"Of course not. Everyone I know is my size. Regular size, that is," said Bigelow.

"*I'm* regular size," said the lady, whose name was Mrs. Pimberly.

"Oh, no," said Bigelow politely. "I'm regular size, I'm sure. You are just very small."

Bigelow started to sit down.

"Not on my house!" shouted Mrs. Pimberly.

Bigelow found a place that was not Mrs. Pimberly's house. Then he sat down. Mrs. Pimberly walked up close to him.

"I thought giants were very fierce," said Mrs. Pimberly.

"Well, they are, I believe," said Bigelow. "Being just regular size, I'm not very fierce myself. In fact, I'm afraid of just about everything."

"You are?" asked Mrs. Pimberly.

"Yes, I'm afraid so," said Bigelow.

Mrs. Pimberly looked Bigelow up and down.

"It wouldn't matter that you're afraid of things except that you're a giant. And," she added, "giants are very brave people."

"Well, it matters to *me* that I'm afraid," he said sadly.

"You know what I think?" said Mrs. Pimberly. "I think that if you acted very brave, you'd feel very brave."

"You do?" said Bigelow.

"Sure," said Mrs. Pimberly. "I bet if you went around shouting a giant sort of shout that would make you feel braver."

"What's a giant sort of shout?" asked Bigelow.

"Well, the only one I can think of is *Fee Fi Fo Fum*," said Mrs. Pimberly. "All giants know that one. Why don't you practice it for a while?" she said, walking into her house.

While Mrs. Pimberly was gone, Bigelow practiced saying *Fee Fi Fo Fum.* He felt pretty silly practicing a giant sort of thing. After all, he knew that he was just regular size. But anything was worth trying.

Bigelow was saying *Fee Fi Fo Fum* very softly to himself when Mrs. Pimberly came out again.

158

"FEE FI FO FUM!" said Bigelow in his
loudest voice.

Mrs. Pimberly threw up her arms. "Goodness,"
she said. "You really scared me. That's a very
good shout. I'm sure it will make you feel much,
much braver."

Bigelow stood up. He ducked a little, in
case he was going to hit his head on the sky.
But he didn't. That made him feel a little
braver.

Bigelow turned his head. He saw his shadow
on the ground. Usually Bigelow was afraid of
his shadow. Now he said, "Fee Fi Fo Fum!"

"Would you like to come home with me?"
Bigelow asked Mrs. Pimberly. "You could have
supper with my parents and me."

Mrs. Pimberly thought about how big
Bigelow's parents must be.

"I never visit anyone," she said, not
wanting to hurt his feelings. "I never go
anywhere. I never travel or anything. In fact,"
she said with a sad sigh, "I've never even
been on a train. I think it would be best if you
visited me instead of the other way around."

"Then I'll go on home for supper now, if
it's all right with you," said Bigelow.

"It's quite all right," Mrs. Pimberly told
him. "But do try to come back tomorrow to
practice being brave."

"I will," said Bigelow. "And thank you for
Fee Fi Fo Fum."

When Bigelow got home, supper was ready.
It was alphabet soup again.

"Fee Fi Fo Fum," said Bigelow.

"What, dear?" asked his mother.

Bigelow looked at the soup.

"Fee Fi Fo Fum," he said again, louder,
and started to eat the soup. He ate it all,
all but the letters. He left them just to be
on the safe side. He ate up the soup part,
though. Mrs. Pimberly would be very proud of
that.

"Are we giants?" Bigelow asked his mother after they had finished dinner.

"Giants?" said his mother. "Oh, no, dear. Giants are very big. We're just regular size."

"I met someone very small today," said Bigelow. "She thought I was a giant."

"That's nice, dear. You're growing up to be a very tall boy. That's probably what she meant," his mother said.

"Oh," said Bigelow.

He thought that over for a while. Then he said one more *Fee Fi Fo Fum* and went up to bed.

The next morning, after breakfast, Bigelow began playing with his trains. Then suddenly he jumped up.

"Trains!" he shouted excitedly. "Mrs. Pimberly has never been on a train!"

He got a big box. He put his trains inside. Then he carried the box over to Mrs. Pimberly's house.

He set them up as fast as he could. Then he leaned down to Mrs. Pimberly's window.

"Good morning," he whispered softly, so as not to frighten her.

Mrs. Pimberly looked out. "Goodness!" she said. "A real train!"

"All aboard!" called Bigelow.

Mrs. Pimberly ran out of her house. She climbed into one of the train cars. Bigelow got it going. Away went the train and away went Mrs. Pimberly, round and round and round.

"I'm really traveling!" Mrs. Pimberly said happily. "And I'm traveling on a real train!" She waved to Bigelow each time the train came around to where he was sitting.

Bigelow was so busy waving back to Mrs. Pimberly that he forgot to be afraid of the clouds or the sky or his shadow. He even forgot to say *Fee Fi Fo Fum*.

After all, giants are very brave people!

To be read by the teacher

Don't Hide

by Norah Smaridge

The thunder makes a rumbling sound
In dark and stormy weather
As if a giant grabbed some clouds
And banged them hard together.
Why is it that some girls and boys
Are scared of it, I wonder
It's only noise, and THEY can make
Much noisier noise than thunder.

Beech Leaves

by James Reeves

In autumn down the beechwood path
The leaves lie thick upon the ground.
It's there I love to kick my way
And hear the crisp and crashing sound.

I am a giant, and my steps
Echo and thunder to the sky.
How the small creatures of the woods
Must quake and cower as I go by!

This brave and merry noise I make
In summer also when I stride
Down to the shining, pebbly sea
And kick the frothing waves aside.

SECTION TWO

Angela and the Bear

by Susan Jeschke

One day Angela went to the zoo.

Near the gate there was a man selling things. Angela decided to buy some crayons.

"Good choice," the man said. "Those are magic crayons. They make magic pictures."

Angela put the crayons into her pocket. Then she went to see Lola, her favorite bear.

"If only I had a bear of my own," she thought.

But every time she asked for one her father would say, "No. You can't always have something just because you want it."

"Anyway, today I have magic crayons," she said to herself. "That's something."

168

Later, at home, she took out her crayons and began to draw a bear.

"How real it looks!" she said.

The more she looked, the more real it became.

"Oh, you are real! Come out! Come out of the picture!" Angela cried.

To her great surprise, the bear did just that! Once outside, he grew and grew until he was a full-size bear.

"My bear! My very own bear!" Angela cried. "But where will I hide you?"

Bear nodded to the picture.

"Terrific idea!" Angela said. "Then I can take you with me wherever I go."

Bear made himself small enough to get back into the picture. And, wherever Angela went, the picture and Bear went too.

Bear was always happy when they did new things. There were many things to keep Bear happy in the summer and fall. But for Bear, winter was the best time of all. He loved the snow.

Then spring came and it rained almost every day. They had to stay at home. Angela did everything she could to please Bear. But it wasn't until she showed him a book with bears that he began to smile.

This gave Angela an idea. She threw up her hands and laughed with joy.

"We will go to see Lola!" she said.

Angela got into her coat. Bear got into his picture. Then they set out.

170

Lola remembered Angela right away. Then Angela took out her picture.

Without waiting for Angela to say "Come out, Bear," Bear jumped out.

Bear and Lola stared at each other. Then they both let out a happy growl. They growled once more. Then they jumped into the pool.

"OK, time to go home," said Angela.

Bear shook his head no.

"But you must. You are my bear!" she said.

She tried to get Bear back into the picture. But Bear didn't want to leave Lola. Finally Angela gave up and ran home.

"It's just not fair, he's mine," she cried.

The next day, Angela's father read her something from the newspaper. It was about a new bear that had suddenly appeared at the zoo. Nobody seemed to know where it had come from.

"I know all about it," Angela said. "He's mine!"

"Oh, I see. Well, I would like to have a look at *your* bear. How about you and I going to the zoo?" he said.

Around the cage were lots and lots of people. Everyone stared at the new bear.

"What do you think of our terrific new bear?" the keeper said. "Lola really likes him."

"I like him too," Angela thought. "I must get him back."

Every day Angela went to the zoo. She begged and begged and begged, but Bear would not leave Lola.

Finally Angela had an idea. She took her magic crayons and drew a picture of a very cold place. She drew snow and ice. She even drew a few fish. Then she waited for a warm night and set out for the zoo. She took a real fish, a string, and the picture.

Lola and Bear were both asleep when Angela got there. Angela tied the string around the fish and threw it into the cage. It tapped Bear right on the nose. He got up and followed the smell.

Angela pulled the fish toward the picture.
Just as Bear reached for it, she pulled it
under the picture. Bear stared at the picture.
He couldn't take his eyes off it. Then he
grew smaller and smaller. He grew so small he
fit right back into the picture.

The next morning the TV news said that
Bear was gone from the zoo.

"Everyone is going to be really sad if
this bear isn't found," her father said.

Angela tried to make her father feel
better. "Well, everyone can't have something
just because they want it. Besides, they
might find him," she said.

174

When she went back to her room, Bear was
sitting up.

"We're going on a picnic. I know how you
love picnics," Angela said.

Bear turned away from Angela and went back
into his picture. Angela was getting worried.

She put the picture into the picnic basket
and walked to the zoo. Her father was right.
Everyone was sad. She heard people saying, "I
hope that terrific new bear is all right. This
zoo is so lonely without him."

The keeper was sitting on a bench.

"I'm going to sit here until that bear is
back," he said.

Lola was hiding. She would not come out.

Angela found a secret spot for the picnic. She took the picture out of her basket.

"Come out, Bear," she said. But he wouldn't.

It was a very lonely picnic for Angela. She just sat and looked at Bear looking at her.

Finally Angela couldn't stand Bear's sad face anymore.

"I like you best when you are happy!" she said, putting the picture into her basket.

Then she went back to the zoo.

Everyone had gone home but the keeper. He was asleep.

"Bear," she whispered to the picture, "come out. I've brought you back to Lola."

176

Bear jumped out and hugged Angela. Then he growled and growled and growled. The growling got the keeper up. He saw Bear and led him back into the cage.

"Good-by, Bear," Angela whispered. "I love you."

Bear and Lola smiled at Angela.

Then Angela threw her picture into a garbage can and ran home.

Comprehension Check

1. What did Angela buy from the man who was selling things at the zoo?
2. Why do you think Angela took Bear to see Lola?
3. Do you think Angela was right to take Bear back to the zoo and Lola? Why do you think as you do?
4. If you had a box of magic crayons like Angela's, what would you draw? Explain why.

CRAYONS

by Marchette Chute

I've colored a picture with crayons.
    I'm not very pleased with the sun.
I'd like it much stronger and brighter
    And more like the actual one.
I've tried with the crayon that's yellow,
    I've tried with the crayon that's red.
But none of it looks like the sunlight
    I carry around in my head.

178

A Brand-new Beautiful Me

by Madeline Sunshine

Look at me! Just look at me! Don't feel shy. It's all right to stare. To tell the truth, I find that I stare at me, myself. In fact, I can't take my eyes off me. Why, you may ask? Well, if you don't mind my saying so, I'm beautiful! But here again, I must tell the truth. I wasn't always as beautiful as I am today.

But wait! I really should begin at the beginning.

It all started at a picnic. I went on the picnic with some people I'd met that very same day. At the end of the picnic, we all got back into the car.

179

Then, for no reason at all, someone threw me out of the car. Just like that—they threw me out! Never in my life had anyone been so mean. I was left on a country road all by myself. I felt terrible, really terrible. If I hadn't been so angry, I might have cried.

Well, I sat on that country road for a long while. I thought about my life. I wondered what would become of me.

Soon a big wind came. The wind blew and blew. It blew me clear across the road.

I looked around. Where was I, I wondered.
But the truth is, I was too tired to find out
just then. So I found myself a soft bed of
leaves. Then I went to sleep.

The next morning a boy ran up to me.

"Ugh!" he said. "How did *this* get in our
yard?"

Can you imagine! He was talking about me.
What a terrible thing to say!

He picked me up.

I shut my eyes because I was so frightened.

He threw me into a big box.

I was really frightened now.

Then he began walking out of the yard.

When I finally opened my eyes again, I saw
lots of others just like me in the box.

"Where are we going?" I screamed.

The boy didn't answer.

"What are you doing with me?" I screamed
again.

Still there was no answer.

At last he stopped walking. Now we were
right in front of someone's house. The boy
handed the box (with me in it) to a tall woman.

"Here," he said. "This is for the
recycling drive."

"Recycling drive!" I screamed. "What's a
recycling drive?" I was more frightened than
ever.

I stayed with the tall woman for a few days.
Then one morning a truck stopped at the tall
woman's house. Everyone in my box looked up.
The sign on the truck said "Recycling Will
Keep Our Town Clean."

"Hmmm," I thought. "Recycling has
something to do with keeping towns clean."

That was fine with me. I like it when
things are clean.

The woman handed the box, with me in it, to
the man who drove the truck. Then off we went!

The ride was a long one. It was hot in the
truck. But I made a lot of friends along the way.

Finally we reached the end of our trip. My friends and I were taken out of the truck. We were brought into a big room. People worked on us for hours and hours and hours.

And that was the beginning of a brand-new beautiful me! I found out what recycling means too. You see, *I* was recycled. I used to be just an old newspaper littering roads and backyards. But look at me now!

Here I am!

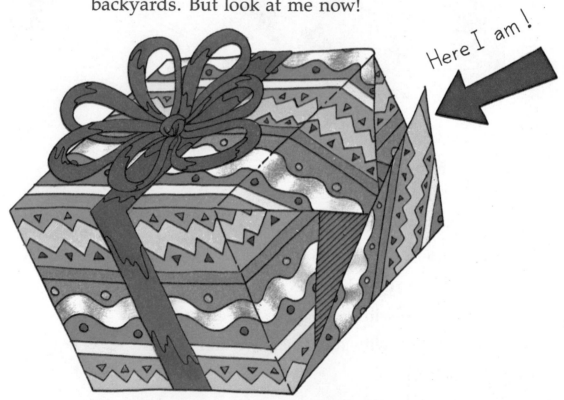

To find out exactly what recycling is, read the next two pages. Then you can help someone like me find a brand-new beautiful life.

More About Recycling

BEFORE RECYCLING   AFTER RECYCLING

You just read about a newspaper that was recycled. What is recycling? *Recycling* is a way of changing something you *can't* use into something you *can* use.

Most often trash is what's recycled. *Trash* is anything people throw away. Old cans, bottles, and newspapers are kinds of trash.

Trash pollutes our world. This means it makes our world dirty. Recycling helps to keep our world clean.

When you finish reading a newspaper, you can recycle it. A newspaper can be made into anything from writing paper to an egg box.

What do you think can be done with old glass bottles? Old glass bottles are crushed up into very tiny pieces. These tiny pieces are then used to pave streets and sidewalks.

You can help your city, town, or neighborhood become a nicer place to live. How? You can take part in the recycling that's going on around you.

Many neighborhoods have recycling centers. These are places where people bring the trash they want recycled. Find out if your neighborhood has one. If it does, find out what kind of trash is recycled there.

As the story said, recycling can give something old a brand-new beautiful life.

Comprehension Check

1. In "A Brand-new Beautiful Me," what happens to the newspaper after the picnic?
2. Why do you think the boy says "Ugh!" when he sees the newspaper in his yard? Why does he take the newspaper to the tall woman's house?
3. Do you think the boy was smart to take part in a recycling drive? Why or why not?
4. What is *recycling?* How does recycling help to keep our world clean?
5. Tell about some other things you can do to help keep your neighborhood clean.

Skill Check

Which of the three words below each sentence belongs in the blank? Use the meaning of each sentence and the consonants.

1. I used to be an old newspaper littering
   r___ ___ds and backyards.
   a. streets   b. roads   c. roots
2. Old glass bo__ttle__s are crushed up into very tiny pieces.
   a. batters   b. windows   c. bottles

What's the Big Idea?

Many paragraphs have a main idea. The **main idea** tells what the paragraph is about. The sentence that tells the main idea often comes at the beginning of the paragraph. It may sometimes come in the middle or at the end of the paragraph. The other sentences in the paragraph add details. The details tell more about the main idea.

Read this paragraph.

Some animals run fast, but the cheetah runs the fastest. A race horse can run 19 miles (about 30 kilometers) per hour but a cheetah can run 32 miles (about 52 kilometers) per hour! It uses its great speed when it is hunting. The cheetah can keep running fast for a long time. It can catch almost anything.

Which sentence in the paragraph tells the main idea? If you said, "Some animals run fast, but the cheetah runs the fastest," you were right. That sentence tells what the paragraph is about. What details do the other sentences give you about the speed of the cheetah?

Practice

Read the next paragraph. Find the sentence that tells the main idea. Then find the details that tell more about the main idea.

Upstairs, many reporters were writing stories. Downstairs, the presses were humming. Over one hundred people were printing the stories. Outside, drivers filled their trucks and sped off. Many people help to put out a newspaper.

1. What is the main idea of the paragraph?
2. Look at this sentence: "Over one hundred people were printing the stories." Is this sentence a detail? Why or why not?
3. What is another detail in the paragraph?

Pay attention to the main ideas and details in the next story, "The Spider Plant." They will help you understand the story better.

The Spider Plant

by Yetta Speevack

Carmen liked living in her new neighborhood. But there was one thing she couldn't get used to. There weren't many trees or flowers in this part of town. Where she used to live everything was green and growing. Now if she wanted to see flowers, she had to go to the flower market. If she wanted to see trees, she had to go to the park. That helped. But it wasn't the same as seeing trees outside her window every morning. And it wasn't the same as having a backyard filled with flowers.

That's why Carmen tried so hard to get the plant-watering job at school. When she did, she took extra special care of the plants.

190

One day, while watering the spider plant, Carmen saw her teacher watching her.

"Why don't I give you a little spider plant to take home?" Miss Hall said. "You deserve one for taking such good care of our plants."

"Oh, thank you," Carmen said excitedly.

Then suddenly she thought of something that made her feel very sad.

"I can't have a plant at home," she told Miss Hall. "We have no sunny windows in our apartment."

Miss Hall explained that spider plants do not really need to be kept in sunny places.

"This plant will do well under an electric light," she said.

At once Carmen was happy again. She would finally have something green and growing to look at and care for.

That afternoon Carmen went home with her very own spider plant.

"Mama, Mama," she called as she ran into the house. "*Mira*—look what I have!"

"Where did you get the plant?" her mother asked.

"My teacher helped me make it from one of *her* plants. She gave it to me because I take such good care of all the plants in school. And guess what?" Carmen said excitedly. "This plant doesn't need a sunny window. My teacher says it will do well under an electric light."

"I hope it grows here," Mama said with a smile.

192

Carmen began to look for a place for her plant.

First she looked in the living room. But the electric light there was very high up. It was too far away to do the plant much good.

Next Carmen went on to her bedroom. Her room had a small window that looked out onto another building. But it didn't let in much light. No, her room would never do.

She was standing there holding the plant when she thought of Pedro's fish tank. The tank had an electric light to keep the fish warm.

"Just the place!" she thought.

Carmen rushed over to the fish tank. She moved it to one side. Then she put her little spider plant under the light.

She had almost forgotten what she had done when Pedro came home.

"Who did this?" she heard him call in his loud, older-brother voice. Only then did Carmen remember the plant. She ran over to Pedro.

"It's my plant. Miss Hall gave it to me. I wanted it to have some light," she said.

"Not here!" Pedro shouted. "If you need a light, get one of your own!"

Carmen took her plant off the table. She was really angry at Pedro. She felt sure he cared more for his fish than for her.

The next day Carmen looked at her plant. She washed its leaves and watered the soil. But the plant did not look well. It needed light. She would have to find a way to give it some.

"Where's Pedro?" Carmen asked Mama. She would beg Pedro to let her use his electric light for just ten minutes.

"He's working," Mama said.

Carmen wondered if she should use the light anyway. It wouldn't hurt Pedro's fish. He wouldn't even have to know about it. At last she made up her mind. She pushed the tank over to one side. Then she put the spider plant right under the electric light.

A few minutes later Mrs. Morales came in. She lived next door. She asked Carmen to take care of her daughter Maria while she went to the market.

Carmen went off with Mrs. Morales. She stayed with Maria until almost five o'clock. When she finally left the Morales apartment, Pedro was coming up the steps. She saw him and remembered her plant. But it was too late! Pedro ran inside the house and rushed over to his fish tank.

"Oh, no! Not again!" he shouted. And before Carmen could grab the plant away, he knocked it off the table.

Carmen watched as the pot broke into thousands of pieces. She was too surprised to say a word. All she could think about was her plant. It had meant so much to her. It had meant as much as Pedro's fish meant to him. Now it was gone. There was nothing she could do about it.

She ran into her bedroom and shut the door.

A little later Carmen heard Papa come home from work. She heard him talking first to Mama and then to Pedro. Finally he called her out of the bedroom.

"Look, Carmen," said Papa. "Only the little
pot is broken. The plant is still good. Put
your plant into this yellow bowl. Mama says
you've always liked this bowl."

Carmen took the little bowl. Then she put
some broken pieces from the old flower pot
into it. That's what she had seen her teacher
do. Next she filled the bowl with some of the
soil her mother had picked up from the floor.

Papa, Mama, and Pedro watched as she put the
spider plant into the little bowl.

198

"I can see that you don't have enough soil," Papa said to Carmen. "Go to the market tomorrow and buy a small bag. I'll give you the money."

"I'll buy you a watering can," said Mama.

"I'll buy you a little electric light," Pedro added, trying to be friends again.

Carmen smiled. It was like a birthday, with presents all around. She had never been so happy.

"Soon we will watch my spider plant bloom," she said excitedly. "And its little white flower will be a *thank you* to all of you."

Comprehension Check

1. Who gave Carmen the spider plant?
2. Do you think the spider plant was important to Carmen? Why or why not?
3. Do you think Carmen should have used her brother's fish tank light? Why or why not?
4. Do you think Carmen's brother should have thrown the plant off the table? Why or why not?
5. Have you ever taken care of a plant? Tell how you cared for it.

Skill Check

Read these sentences from "The Spider Plant." Then answer the questions below.

There weren't many trees or flowers in this part of town. Where she used to live everything was green and growing. Now if she wanted to see flowers, she had to go to the flower market. If she wanted to see trees, she had to go to the park.

1. Which sentence tells the main idea of this paragraph?
2. Which two sentences give details that tell about the main idea?

NOTHING MUCH HAPPENED TODAY

by Mary Blount Christian

Mrs. Mayberry dashed home from the market. She dashed home from the market to tell her children about seeing the police chase a robber. She had never seen police chasing a robber before.

She turned the corner. As she did, her mouth flew open. Soap bubbles—hundreds of soap bubbles—were pouring from the front window.

She couldn't believe her eyes. Was this really her house? She stared for a minute. Then she opened the door as fast as she could.

"What happened?" she demanded, staring at Steven, Elizabeth, and Alan. "What happened here?"

Steven shrugged. "Nothing much, really," he said.

"But look at those bubbles!" she yelled.

Steven shrugged again.

Elizabeth shrugged too. "I guess we used too much soap when we washed Chester," she said.

"The dog? You took soap and washed the dog? Why did you wash the dog?" Mrs. Mayberry demanded to know. She stared first at Steven, then at Elizabeth, and finally at Alan.

At last Alan, the youngest of the three children, answered.

"Chester got honey all over his fur," he explained.

Mrs. Mayberry set her bags down. "I was only gone a few minutes. How could Chester get honey in his fur?"

"He was chasing the cat when he bumped into the honey jar," Steven piped in. "The honey poured out all over him."

Mrs. Mayberry gasped. "Cat? Cat? We don't have a cat," she cried.

"You might say it was a visiting cat,"
Steven explained. "It came through the window
that we opened to let the smoke out."

Mrs. Mayberry held her head. "Smoke! What
smoke?" she demanded.

"The smoke from the oven when the cake
poured out of the pan," Elizabeth went on.

Mrs. Mayberry waved her arms excitedly.

"Why were you making a cake?" she asked.

"For the school bake sale," Alan said.

"But I made one this morning!" Mrs.
Mayberry shouted.

"We know," said Steven. "We were making a
new one. The cake you made fell on the floor
when the police bumped into the table."

"Police! What police?" Mrs. Mayberry cried.

"The police that were chasing the robber,"
Alan told her.

"MY robber?" Mrs. Mayberry gasped excitedly.
"I mean the robber I saw at the market? But how
did the police and a robber knock over my cake?"

Steven smiled. "That's easy," he said. "The
robber dashed around and around the table. The
police ran around and around after him. They
bumped into the table. The cake was on the
table. It fell on the floor. Then the robber
slid on the icing."

Elizabeth added, "And when the robber fell,
he hit his head on Alan's head. And you know
how hard Alan's head is."

"I know, I know," gasped Mrs. Mayberry. "Let me see now. The robber ran in and the police chased him. They bumped into the table and knocked over the cake. When you made a new one, smoke came out of the oven. Then you opened the window and a cat ran in.

"Chester chased the cat, and the jar of honey poured out all over him. The honey got in his fur. When you washed him, you used too much soap. The soap made bubbles—hundreds of bubbles. The bubbles poured out of the window."

"That's right!" the three children said excitedly. "And that's when you came home."

"I know I couldn't have been gone more than twenty minutes!" Mrs. Mayberry whispered.

"Well, we told you nothing much happened today," Steven said.

Comprehension Check

1. What did Mrs. Mayberry dash home to tell her children about?
2. Do you think Steven really meant that nothing much happened that day? Why or why not?
3. Do you think that Mrs. Mayberry was surprised by all that happened while she was gone? Why do you think as you do?
4. Have you ever had a day where a lot of funny things happened all at once? Tell about it.

Skill Check

In the story you just read, in what order did the following things take place?

1. Smoke came out of the oven.
2. Chester got honey in his fur.
3. The cat came through the window.
4. Mrs. Mayberry came home.
5. The police chased the robber.

Navajo Pet

by Patricia Miles Martin

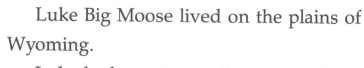

Luke Big Moose lived on the plains of Wyoming.

Luke had a pet goat. Every morning the goat would watch while Luke climbed up on a big yellow bus. The bus took Luke down the road to the schoolhouse. The goat would stare after the bus until it was way out of sight.

Danny Long John also lived on the plains of Wyoming. He had a pet too. He had an old horse.

Luke liked everything about Wyoming except Danny. He didn't like Danny's horse much either.

In school the one who behaved best was asked to carry out all the old papers. The papers had to be dropped in a deep hole behind the schoolhouse. Luke usually shoved Danny Long John at least once a day. So Luke never got to carry the papers out. But Danny sometimes carried them.

While Luke and Danny were in school, Danny's horse and Luke's goat went everywhere together. Sometimes they went to the school. Most of the time they took a faraway path over the flatland to the red-brown bluffs.

But in the afternoon, when Luke came home from school, his goat was always in front of the house waiting for him. Some days Danny's horse was there too.

One afternoon Danny came to Luke's house.
He was holding a rope.

"Why do you keep taking my horse?" he yelled.

"Why does he follow my goat?" Luke asked.

Danny shoved the goat. The goat butted him.

"That goat knows who his enemies are," Luke
said. "That's more than your old horse knows."

Danny put his rope around the horse's neck.
He jumped on his back and trotted away.

Later Luke was playing with his goat. The
horse trotted into sight again. It ran up to
them. Fast as he could, Danny dashed over too.

"You've got my horse again," he shouted.

"Keep your horse away from my goat," Luke
broke in.

On Sunday morning Luke went outside to the sheep pen. He opened the gate. Luke and the goat led the sheep through the gate. They were looking for a patch of green where the sheep might feed. They took a path that passed Danny's house. His old horse was tied to a post beside the door.

Near the bluffs Luke found a place, and there they stopped. The sheep nibbled on wild grasses. The goat ate too.

In the middle of the morning, Luke heard a neighing sound. He looked around. There was Danny's horse, a rope trailing behind him. The horse ate with the goat and the sheep.

On the way home that evening, Luke passed
Danny's house again. Danny was not in sight.
Luke led the horse to Danny's door. He tied
the rope to the post and left him there.

Then he and the goat hurried on with the
sheep.

On Monday afternoon when Luke came home
from school, his goat was not waiting at the
house.

"My goat is gone," Luke said to his grandpa.
"I can't find it and I've looked everywhere. I
think Danny Long John took it."

"Get the goat back," his grandpa said.

Luke dashed away. He headed for Danny's house. He ran through a patch of wild flowers. Then he stopped in front of a small gray house.

"Danny, my goat is gone. I came to get it," he called.

Danny's mother answered. "Danny's horse is gone," she said. "He's looked for it everywhere. Now he's on his way to your house."

Luke started running home. Just then he saw Danny. Danny was carrying a rope.

"You took my goat," Luke said. He walked up and shoved Danny.

"You took my horse," Danny said, shoving Luke back.

The two boys were ready to fight when a horse neighed.

"That sounds like my horse," Danny said.

Then they heard a goat. *"Baaaaa."*

"That sounds like my goat," Luke said.

The sounds came from far away. The boys ran for a while. Then they stopped and listened. They were sure the animals were somewhere near the schoolhouse. They dashed toward it as fast as they could.

Behind the schoolhouse, the horse was standing and waiting.

"The goat is down in the hole," Danny said.

Luke dropped down into the hole. He tied Danny's rope around the goat's middle. Then together, the two boys pulled the goat up.

Danny took the rope off the goat. The goat butted him.

"That goat doesn't know who his friends are," Danny said.

"That's for sure," Luke said, smiling.

Danny put his rope around the horse's neck and jumped up on his back.

"Get up behind me, Luke," Danny said, patting his horse's neck. "We'll all go home together."

Luke jumped up. The goat walked beside them.

Now and then the goat stopped at a green field. It nibbled a bit of wild grass. The horse nibbled too. Luke and Danny sat waiting while they ate.

The boys headed toward Luke's house. They trotted along the same path they had taken before. They passed a patch of wild grass and a patch of wild flowers.

"If we stick together, we'll always know where our pets are," Danny said.

"We'll stick together," said Luke. "Don't worry. From now on, we'll stick together."

Comprehension Check

1. Which boy had a goat for a pet? Which boy had a horse?
2. Why do you think Danny always looked for his horse at Luke's house?
3. Do you think Luke and Danny worked well together when they pulled the goat out of the hole? Why or why not?
4. Do you think working together helped the two boys become friends? Why or why not?

Literary Unit

Neighbors

by Mary Ann Hoberman

The Cobbles live in the house next door,
In the house with the prickly pine.
Whenever I see them, they ask "How are you?"
And I always answer, "I'm fine."
And I always ask them, "Is Jonathan home?"
(Jonathan Cobble is nine.)
I'm Jonathan Cobble's very best friend
And Jonathan Cobble is mine.

Learning the Meaning of a Word

A <u>dictionary</u> or <u>glossary</u> tells the meaning
of words.

> Frances answered the telephone.
>
> "Hello, is this Frances Fern?" asked
> a voice.
>
> "Yes, it is," said Frances.
>
> "I have good news for you," said the
> voice. "You have just won a wonderful
> prize. It's a huge yucca! I hope you
> like it!"
>
> "That's great," Frances said. "I just
> won a yucca!" Then she cried, "Wait
> a minute! What's a yucca?"

Frances looked in a dictionary to find out
what a yucca is. She knew that the words in
a dictionary are in alphabetical order. Frances
turned to the page on which the words began
with <u>y</u>.

First she looked at the guide words at the top of the page. **Guide words** tell you the first and last entry words on the page.

Under the letter y there was one entry. An **entry** is made up of an entry word, a definition, and sometimes a picture. The **entry word** is the word that is explained. The **definition** tells you what the entry word means. Frances read the definition of yucca and looked at the picture.

yuc ca a green plant that grows in warm areas. It has pointed leaves and whitish flowers. See the picture. **yuc cas.**

yucca

"A yucca is a beautiful plant," she exclaimed. "I think I'll keep it near my window."

1. What are the parts of an entry?
2. What do guide words tell you?

Practice

Turn to the glossary at the back of this book.

1. Find the word bluff.
   a. What are the guide words at the top of the page?
   b. Could the word reward be on this page? Why or why not?
   c. What are the definitions for bluff? Which one explains how the word bluff was used on page 209?
2. Find the word cuddly.
   a. What are the guide words at the top of the page?
   b. Could the word grouch be on this page? Why or why not?
   c. What is the definition of cuddly?

Read the next story, "Cover to Cover." Use your glossary to help you find the meanings of words you don't know.

Cover to Cover

by Helen Benham

Take some terrific stories. Write a short play that can be acted out. Add some games that also teach something. Find a TV or movie star who is interesting to talk about. Get a sports scoop. Throw in some jokes.

Now find some pictures. Pick some that go well with the stories. Make sure the pictures are exciting. They will bring the words to life.

Put all the pictures and words together. Ship them off to be printed. When everything is printed, what will you have? *A magazine!*

It sounds pretty simple, but it's really not. Putting together a magazine is hard work. I know because I work on a magazine five days a week. I am a magazine *editor.*

The readers of my magazine are children. So far most of my readers seem to like the magazine. But before it reaches them, I have a lot of work to do. I have to follow six steps. (I'm glad to say there are other people, like Michael, to help me!)

Step One: Plan

Planning is really the most important step of all. *Planning* means finding things the readers will want to read about. We plan each part of the magazine very carefully.

First we figure out who will be on our cover. Who should it be this week? A sports star? A TV star? A movie star? A rock 'n' roll singer? We have to choose somebody exciting. After all, the cover is the first thing readers will see. We look for someone we can find out more about. That way we can write a story about the person inside the magazine.

If we can, we try to speak with the person we choose for the cover. We look for interesting facts. We ask questions and write down the answers we are given. Sometimes the person can't be reached. Then we have to talk to people who know about that person. These people can be co-workers, family, or friends.

Next we plan all the other stories that will appear in this issue of the magazine. We dig up all the facts we can find about every story. To get the facts, we talk to people. We also do a lot of reading. We go to the library. We read newspapers, books, and other magazines.

Soon time starts running out. We have to move on to the next step.

Step Two: Write

Everything we have planned has to be written. Maybe I will write a play or a magic trick. Michael is good at writing sports stories. So that's what he will do. Other writers will write word games or news stories.

Finally everything is written. Now we are ready to begin Step Three.

Step Three: Edit

All the stories for this issue are written. *We* think most of them are very exciting! Now it's time for us to edit.

Editing means getting everything that has been written ready to be printed. How do we edit? What do we do when we edit?

First we check for mistakes. Did we get the facts straight? Are all the words in the stories spelled right? Will the words fit on this or that page? Will the readers really think this joke is funny? Is there a better way to say that sentence? Answering these questions is what editing is all about.

We edit the last page of the magazine. Then I check the clock. We have to hurry. This issue of the magazine has to be ready soon. There's no more time to make changes. So we go on to Step Four.

Step Four: Choose the Art

This step is where the artists come in. The artists read the stories, plays, and games that have been written. Then we all talk about what kinds of pictures will go with the words. Drawings are made. Pictures are taken. We find a terrific picture for the cover. It has to be one that will make our readers want to read the magazine. Then Step Five begins.

Step Five: Paste Up

It's time for the writers, artists, and me to put the magazine together. We start by going over some of the previous steps even more carefully. We figure out *exactly* what words will go on what page of the magazine. We figure out *exactly* which pictures to put on each page. Then we check to see that the words and pictures still go well together.

When we are happy with the way everything looks, the words and pictures are pasted down on big pieces of cardboard. This is called *paste up*. We all check the pieces of cardboard, or "boards," one last time. We must be sure that everything looks right. Once we are sure, we can go on to Step Six.

Step Six: Ship It!

Our work on this week's issue of the magazine is done. Finally we send the boards to a printer. Thousands of magazines are printed. Soon readers all over the country will have them. We think the magazine looks terrific! We hope our readers think it's terrific too.

The writers, artists, and I take a minute to look at the work we've done. But we don't have much time. We have to get moving right away. We only have two weeks to get the next issue of our magazine together. We have to begin each of the six steps all over again. I look at the clock. Time is running out!

Comprehension Check

1. What are the six steps that Helen follows in order to put together the magazine?
2. Why do you think that Helen says pictures bring the words to life?
3. Which of the six steps do you think is the most difficult? Which do you think would be most fun? Tell why you think as you do.
4. Would you like to help put a magazine together? Why or why not? What job would you like to do?

Skill Check

Turn to the glossary at the back of this book to answer these questions.

Find the words *scoop* and *co-worker*.

a. What are the guide words at the top of each page?
b. Could the word *ostrich* be on the same page as *scoop*? Why or why not? Could it be on the same page as *co-worker*? Why or why not?
c. What are the definitions listed for *scoop* and *co-worker*? Which definition of *scoop* explains how the word was used in the story you just read?

Jenna's Newspaper
by Ida Friedman

CITY NEWS

It was a warm, sunny day. But Jenna Reese felt neither warm nor sunny inside. She felt really terrible! She took a deep breath. Then she started walking home. Soon she had passed the *City News* building.

"It isn't fair!" she thought. "It just isn't fair!"

Jenna had always wanted to be a newspaper writer. She knew she'd be a good one too. But Ms. Martinez at the *City News* had turned her down.

"Why, you're just a child, dear," Ms. Martinez had said. "Come back when you're grown up. Right now, I'm afraid it's impossible."

"Nothing is impossible," Jenna thought. She kicked a stone out of her way and kept on walking. Then, all of a sudden, the idea hit her.

"I'll start my own newspaper!" she exclaimed excitedly. "I'll write stories. Maybe Marty, Kim, and Michael will help too. We'll write about things kids *really* want to read."

In no time at all she got her friends together. She told them her idea. They thought it was exciting too. By the next day each had written a story for Jenna's newspaper.

Marty loved sports. So he wrote a sports story. Kim wrote a story about what animal keepers do. Her neighbor was an animal keeper at the city zoo. Michael's story was about the interesting things that always seemed to happen in their neighborhood.

Only Jenna hadn't written her story yet. She hadn't come up with an idea that was special enough. She was getting a little worried.

In fact, she was getting worried about something else too. Real newspapers were printed. They were delivered or sold at newsstands. All Jenna had were stories.

"How will I ever turn these stories into a newspaper?" she wondered.

She asked Michael and Kim and Marty. None of them seemed to know either. Jenna put her hands in her pockets. At first everything had seemed so exciting. Now everything seemed terrible. She was more worried than ever. She walked back and forth across the room. Then, at last, she turned to her friends.

"The newsstand!" she said. "That's it! I'll ask Louie at the newsstand to help us. He sells newspapers. I'm sure he knows how they are put together."

Without waiting for an answer Jenna sped off. She ran as quickly as she could. When she finally reached the newsstand, she was all out of breath.

"Louie," she cried. "You've got to help me."

"Help?" the man said in a grumpy voice. "Why do you need my help?"

"I'm starting a newspaper," Jenna said. "I need you to tell me how to put it together."

"Me!" Louie said in his same grumpy voice. "What do I look like, a printer? I don't print newspapers. I just sell them!"

"Of course!" exclaimed Jenna. "A printer! That's who will help me. There must be a print shop around here!"

Quick as a flash she sped down the block. Then she sped down another block. She passed a toy store and a bake shop along the way. Any other day Jenna would have stopped to look in the windows. But now there was no time for that!

234

"A print shop," thought Jenna. "I've got to find a print shop." She turned the corner. Then suddenly she stopped short.

"I found it!" she cried happily. "Loretta's Print Shop!" And in a flash Jenna was off again.

The bell above the shop door rang as Jenna entered.

"Are you Loretta?" she asked the woman inside, trying to catch her breath.

"Yes, I am," said the woman. "May I help you?"

Jenna explained all about her newspaper. "So you see, the stories are all ready. Except for mine," she added quickly. "Now all I need to know is how to put a newspaper together."

"The fact is, I may be able to help you," said Loretta. "I'm a printer, so I can do the printing. But printing costs money."

"I don't have any money," Jenna said sadly. She thought for a minute. "Please print my newspaper," she begged. "If you do, I could put a picture of your shop on the front page. Then lots of people would come here. What do you say?"

"I don't know," Loretta answered.

"I'd help you all I could," Jenna added. Her eyes begged the woman to say yes.

236

"Well," the woman said, "I'm not sure I can decide so quickly. Why don't you let me think about it for a little while. Check back with me in twenty minutes."

"Thank you," Jenna exclaimed, and she walked out of the shop.

When she got outside, Jenna sat down and began to wait. She wished time would hurry up. Waiting around felt awful. It seemed as if hours and hours and hours had passed. Really it was only about five minutes. Finally Jenna couldn't stand it anymore. She stood up and rushed back into the shop.

"Young lady, you've got yourself a deal,"
Loretta said as soon as she spotted Jenna.
"Come back tomorrow and bring your stories.
Then we'll get to work."

"What about a picture of your shop?" Jenna
asked.

"I once drew one," said Loretta. "We can
use that."

Jenna flashed her happiest smile. She went
over and hugged the woman. Then she started for
home. Now there was only one thing left for
Jenna to do. She had to write a special story
for the front page. And, at long last, she knew
exactly what it would be.

The next few days were really exciting. Jenna and her friends helped Loretta print up lots of copies of the newspaper. They even gave it the name *Kid News*. When they were finished, everyone felt very proud. The newspaper looked terrific.

There was Marty's sports story. There was Kim's story about being an animal keeper. There was Michael's story about their neighborhood. There was the picture Loretta drew. It showed the inside of her shop. And then there was Jenna's special front-page story. "How We Started Our Own Newspaper," it read, "by Jenna Reese."

The kids and Loretta delivered copies of the newspaper all over town. They even delivered some copies to grumpy Louie, who promised to give them out at his newsstand.

Jenna felt very proud of the work she and her friends had done. Her parents were feeling proud too. They invited everybody over for a big "Happy Newspaper" party.

All through the party, Jenna's telephone kept ringing. Friends from school and from around the neighborhood were calling. They had all seen copies of Jenna's newspaper. And every one of them wanted to write stories for it.

Jenna smiled as she answered each call. This had been the best day of her life. She thought about the *City News* and about Ms. Martinez. She wondered if the woman had seen *Kid News*. She wondered if now Ms. Martinez thought as Jenna did, that *nothing is impossible!*

Comprehension Check

1. What had Jenna always wanted to be?
2. Why did Jenna decide to start her own newspaper?
3. Why do you think Jenna felt that nothing is impossible?
4. If you were writing a story for a newspaper, what would it be about? Explain why.

Skill Check

Look at the words below. Pick out the root word in each.

turned	begged	wanted
stories	waiting	stopped
passed	kicked	delivered

The Way to Go

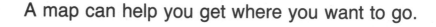

A map can help you get where you want to go.

Dear Dragon,

    I'm glad you want to work for me.
I would like to meet you. Can you come
to my house right away? I have sent you
a map to help you get here.

                        Prince Igor

    The dragon jumped up happily. This
was the letter she had been waiting
for. She grabbed her hat and coat.
Then she dashed off. She followed the
map all the way to Igor's house.

    Look at the map that the dragon followed. Her
dragon prints tell you which way she went.

Where did the dragon start her journey? If you said at her cave, you were right. How many trees did she pass before turning?

The dragon read the map correctly. Soon she reached Igor's house. She hurried inside. Igor was waiting.

"How do you do? I understand you are looking for a dragon," she said politely. She added, "I'm the best there is!"

Prince Igor smiled. "In that case," he replied, "the job is yours!"

What can you find out from a map?

Practice

Look at the map the dragon followed. Then answer these questions.

1. How many buildings did the dragon pass before she reached Igor's house?
2. What did the dragon pass right after the bridge?
3. What is across from the motel?
4. What is under the bridge?

You will have a chance to see how well you can read signs and maps in the next story. Read "Eddie Couldn't Find the Elephants" and see how well you find your way around the zoo.

Eddie Couldn't Find the Elephants

by Edith Battles

One day Eddie and his father decided to go
to the zoo. On the way over there Eddie said,
"I don't need to go to school anymore. Animals
don't read. So I don't need to read. I'll live
at the zoo and show people the way to the
animals. I'll take them everywhere. It will be
a wonderful life!"

"OK," replied Eddie's father. "Start with me.
What animals will you show me first?"

"Elephants," said Eddie.

Eddie looked up at the signs. He could follow
the arrows. But the truth is, he couldn't read
the words. Finally he saw one that looked like
Elephants.

"This way to the elephants," Eddie said, pointing a path out to his father.

Eddie and his father walked down the path a while. They saw a refreshment stand. But the elephants were nowhere in sight.

"We need some apple juice before we look at the elephants," Eddie said, thinking fast. He looked at all the signs on the refreshment stand. Then he shrugged his shoulders. How in the world would he figure out which words said Apple Juice?

Finally he said, "I'll have this." He pointed toward the sign that said Iced Tea.

"And I'll have this," said Eddie's father. He pointed toward the sign that said Apple Juice.

The clerk at the refreshment stand filled two
cups. Eddie started to drink. That's when he
found out that he had asked for iced tea.

"This isn't what I meant to get," he thought.
Then he turned to his father.

"What's in your cup?" gasped the boy.

"Apple juice. Is your tea good?" asked
Eddie's father.

"Best in the world," replied Eddie. But that
wasn't the truth. He pretended to drink it until
his father walked out of sight. Then Eddie threw
the iced tea into a trash can.

Eddie heard seals barking. He said, "Let's look at the seals on the way to the elephants."

Near the seals Eddie saw a boy getting a bag of food from a machine. The bag looked like peanuts. Eddie loved peanuts.

"I'd like some of that," Eddie said. He put his dimes in the machine and pushed a button. A bag fell out. But there were no peanuts in the bag.

Eddie gasped and held the bag away from him. Whatever was inside of it smelled a lot like *fish!*

He looked around. Some children were feeding fish to the seals. Eddie shrugged his shoulders and walked toward them. Then he tossed his fish to the seals too. He pretended he had meant to feed the seals all the time.

248

Eddie smelled his hands. Ugh! They smelled of fish.

"Let's find a washroom and wash our hands," Eddie said.

"Lead the way to the washroom," replied his father.

They began to walk. Everywhere they looked they saw different signs. Eddie stared at each one. At last he found one that looked like Washrooms. He and his father started down the path it pointed to.

Then suddenly they stopped. There, right in front of them, were three elephants. The elephants were really quite a sight.

"I said I was going to show you the elephants," said Eddie. "And I was telling the truth. Here they are!"

"Why don't we sit down and watch the elephants?" said Eddie's father.

Eddie shrugged his shoulders and walked toward a bench. "No one's sitting on this bench," he said. "I'll just move this sign and—"

"Stop!" gasped his father. But it was too late! Eddie was already sitting down. He found out what the sign on the bench meant all by himself.

"Let's go home," Eddie said quietly.

Cap

Baseball bat

Beach ball

Snow Street

On the way home Eddie saw signs everywhere. But he couldn't pretend anymore. He couldn't figure out what any of the signs said.

"It's good that we're going home early," said Eddie's father. "You need time to pack so that you can move to the zoo tomorrow."

Eddie thought and thought. "How in the world can I move to the zoo now?" he said to himself. At last he turned to his father.

"Maybe I'd better wait," he said. "I can *always* move to the zoo. But I need time to say good-by to everyone at school. I guess maybe I'll live at the zoo next year."

Comprehension Check

1. Why did Eddie say he wanted to live at the zoo?
2. At the beginning of the story, Eddie felt he did not need to know how to read. Do you think he felt that way at the end? Why or why not?

Skill Check

Here is a map of the zoo Eddie and his father visited. The arrows show where they went.

1. Where did Eddie and his father go first? Next? Last?
2. What did they pass along the way?
3. Where didn't they go?

freshments

Washroom

A Quiet Place

Literary Unit

by Rose Blue

Mathew slowly walked up the two flights of
stairs that led to his house. Just as slowly
he opened the front door and walked inside. A
wonderful smell of something cooking led him
into the kitchen where Mama was standing at
the stove, stirring a great big pot of stew.

Mama turned and said, "Hello, Mathew." Then
she continued stirring the pot of stew.

"Hello, Mama," Mathew said softly. He opened
the refrigerator and poured himself a glass of
juice. Then he stood just staring into space.

Mama watched him closely for a long minute.
"Is anything wrong, Mathew?" she finally asked.

Mathew shook his head. "It's really nothing," he said.

"Well, where have you been all day?" his mother wanted to know.

"At the library," Mathew said softly. "It's closing tomorrow."

Mama stopped stirring. "So that's it," she said to herself. "I never realized today was the day." She stirred the pot of stew a little more. Then she turned to Mathew.

"The fact that the library is closing isn't the end of the world," she said. "They're building a brand-new library on the avenue, and it will be opening very soon."

Mathew was quiet.

"You know what?" Mama continued, trying to cheer him up. "Someone told me that in the meantime we're getting a library on wheels. It's called a *bookmobile.* It's a big truck filled with books, and it will come rolling into the neighborhood two times a week. Then when the new library is finished, you'll have a really fine place to go."

Mathew closed his eyes. "Maybe the new library would be fine," he thought. But the bookmobile was something else. It would never be like his special place. It wouldn't have a children's room. And it wouldn't have a yellow chair that squished when you sat on it.

Mathew slowly sipped his juice. He tried to imagine what the bookmobile would be like. But the picture he had of it didn't make him feel too happy. He couldn't help but think how different everything was going to be.

His mother looked over and smiled at him. "Mathew," she said, "we can't stop things from changing no matter how much we'd like to. But wait and see. Some changes turn out to be for the best."

Mathew smiled back at his mother. Maybe she was right. Maybe things wouldn't be so bad. He would have to wait and see.

256

The next morning the bookmobile came around for the first time. Mathew left the house very early. He ran down the avenue as fast as he could. He passed the corner newsstand and waved hello to the woman who worked there. He continued running until at last he spotted the long, green bookmobile. He walked up to the truck, climbed its three little stairs, and walked inside.

Once inside, Mathew checked around the bookmobile, looking for the children's section. There were other people walking around too. They were all squished together because there wasn't a lot of room.

The books in the bookmobile were lined up against the wall on shelves. Mathew walked past some shelves and headed toward the back of the truck. Everywhere he walked, he bumped into somebody or something. Once he even bumped into the librarian.

The more he walked around, the more Mathew realized he'd never find a place to be by himself here. He couldn't stay at the bookmobile the way he could at a real library. When he finally came to the children's section, he looked through the shelves as quickly as he could. He stared at all the bright book covers till his eyes fell on a book with a picture of a boy on it. The boy looked very much like Mathew. Mathew thought it would be nice to read a book about a boy who looked so much like himself.

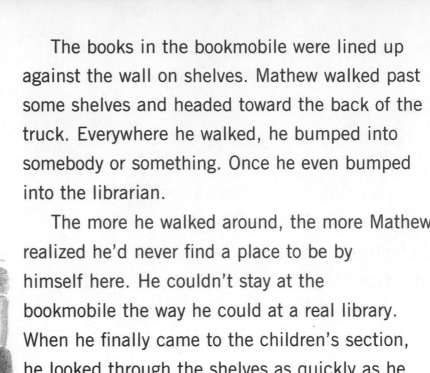

At last Mathew was outside again. He could hardly wait to start his brand-new book. So he ran all the way up the avenue and hurried home. When he got there, Mama was reading the newspaper. He hugged her hello and grabbed some grapes from the bowl on the table. Then he rushed into his room with the brand-new book.

After he looked at the picture of the boy on the front cover, Mathew turned the book over to check the back cover. But just then Mathew's brother, Stevie, opened his sleepy eyes and began to howl. Mama came in to see what was wrong. She picked up the baby and held him, but he kept howling and howling. She put him on the floor. He crawled around a little. Then he began to howl some more.

Mathew was getting very upset. He felt like howling himself. Instead, he picked up his book and took it to the bathroom. He locked the door, sat down on the floor, and looked at the back cover. There were pictures of some houses on a street that looked just like his street. He was still looking at them when his sister, Claudia, began banging at the door.

"Hey, Mathew," she yelled. "Are you planning to stay in there all day?"

Mathew counted to ten. "Now don't get upset," he told himself. Slowly he got up, left the bathroom, and went out the front door. He realized that the house was not the place for him to be just now.

260

Mathew walked down the stairs and out into
the street. Then he went up and down the avenue
and in and out of alleys searching for a quiet
place. But he found none. He wandered around
till he came to the park. It was a sunny day,
and many people were outside. He passed mothers
with their babies, children playing in the
playground, and big kids playing ball. He
crossed a patch of green and kept on going
until he saw a high hill near the back of the
park. Growing on the hill were patches of grass
and beautiful wild flowers.

Mathew climbed up to the top of the hill. There he saw a big tree with four smaller trees around it. The trunk of the big tree made a chair, and Mathew sat down on it. He could hardly believe how comfortable it was. When he looked down he saw people walking along the path. But they looked far away, and he could hardly hear them.

"I found it!" Mathew thought. "I found my special place."

He sat there just watching the breeze stir softly through the leaves. Just then a strong wind blew. It made the leaves shudder as the sun hid behind a dark cloud. When the sun came out once more, Mathew felt no warmer.

Mathew was beginning to worry. It was almost autumn. After autumn came winter and the snow would cover his tree. Autumn would be cold enough. But when the icy winds of winter blew, then where would he go?

Mathew sat close to the tree trunk, holding his book. Then he thought of another boy, a boy in the book he had finished last week. That boy lived way out West a long, long time ago. He thought of how that boy had gone looking for new places and traveled far when the way was hard. He thought of how the boy kept traveling and traveling even while the icy winds of winter blew.

Mathew felt lucky. The icy winds of winter had not come his way yet. It was still summer. He would have time to look for a new place and still be warm.

Tomorrow, right after breakfast, Mathew would start place hunting. He would find a quiet place and have it all ready for winter. He had found an outside place. He could find an inside place too. Then, after autumn and winter, spring would come round again and Mathew could come back to his special tree with its wonderful tree-trunk chair. He rolled over on the soft grass and placed his book in front of him. Then he rested his chin on his hand and opened it up to page one.

Comprehension Check

1. Why was Mathew unhappy in the beginning of the story "A Quiet Place"?
2. Why do you think Mathew missed the old library?
3. Do you think Mathew learned something by the end of the story? Why or why not?
4. Do you have a special place of your own where you like to read or draw or play? Tell why you like this place.

At the Library

by Marchette Chute

This is a lovely place to be.
   The books are everywhere,
And I can read them here, or take
   Them home and read them there.

It is a kind of secret place
   Where I can enter in
And no one tells me where to stop
   Or where I should begin.

The books sit waiting on their shelves,
   As friendly as can be,
And since I am a borrower
   They all belong to me.

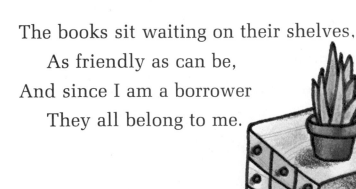

Mystery Messages

by Claire Stevens

Can you read the message below?

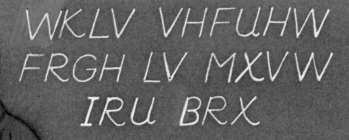

WKLV VHFUHW
FRGH LV MXVW
IRU BRX

It's a message in a mystery language. It
says, "This secret code is just for you." And
that's what this story is about: secret codes
and messages. It tells how to write codes and
how to figure them out. Putting messages into
code is called *encoding*. Figuring out what the
messages mean is called *decoding*.

Detectives have been decoding and encoding
secret codes and messages for many, many years.
You can do it too. Put on your detective caps
and take a look at some of the ways you can
communicate in code.

266

The secret message on the first page of this story was written in an alphabet code. The way it works is really simple. First you write out all twenty-six letters of the alphabet.

Next write the alphabet again, only this time don't start with the letter A. You may start with any letter you like. For example, we've started with the letter D. Put the letter D next to the letter A. Then put the letter E next to the letter B, and so on all the way down the line. When you're finished, the letter A will stand for the letter X.

Now you're ready to use this alphabet code. Here's how. When you want to write the letter *A*, use the letter *D* instead. When you want to write the letter *B*, use the letter *E* instead. For example, you would write the word *happy* like this:

How would you write the word *funny*?

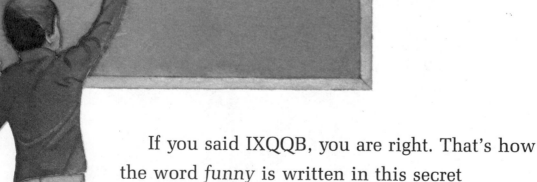

If you said IXQQB, you are right. That's how the word *funny* is written in this secret alphabet code.

You can use this code to exchange secrets with your friends. It's fun to communicate and share mysterious messages.

All right, detectives, are you ready for your next secret code? This one is a real mystery to those who don't know it. In fact, when you write in this code the words are invisible. *Invisible* means they can't be seen. Does this sound impossible? Well, it's not when you use invisible ink. Where do you get invisible ink? You make it. Here's how to do it.

To make invisible ink, all you need is some lemon juice or some orange juice. Put the juice into a small bowl. Use a toothpick or a straw as a pen. Dip your invisible-ink pen into the juice. Then on a piece of white lined paper, begin writing your secret message.

As soon as the juice dries, the words you wrote will become invisible—even to you. How can your secret invisible-ink message be decoded? What you have to do is hold the paper over a light bulb for a little while. Make sure the paper does not touch the light bulb.

The heat of the light bulb will make the invisible letters appear right before your very eyes. This happens because the heat turns the writing on the paper brown. That makes it possible to read.

If you and your detective friends exchange messages written in invisible ink, there will be more on your papers than meets the eye.

Now, if your detective caps are still on,
here's a secret code that really *counts*. It's
made up of numbers.

How does it work? It's a lot like the
alphabet code you read about before. You write
out all the letters in the alphabet. This time,
however, you write numbers next to the alphabet
letters.

A	1	H	8	O	15	V	22
B	2	I	9	P	16	W	23
C	3	J	10	Q	17	X	24
D	4	K	11	R	18	Y	25
E	5	L	12	S	19	Z	26
F	6	M	13	T	20		
G	7	N	14	U	21		

Now you'll be using numbers instead of
letters to spell out your secret messages. For
example, try to read this message:

11 - 5 - 5 - 16 - 9 - 14 - 7
19 - 5 - 3 - 18 - 5 - 20 - 19
9 - 19   6 - 21 - 14

Can you decode this message? That's right,
detectives, it says, "Keeping secrets is fun."
And that's the truth. Secrets are fun to keep
and to exchange.

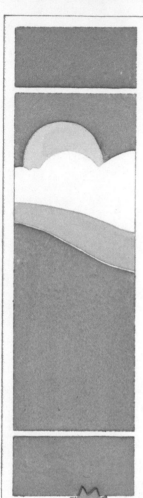

Now here's a secret code you may have already heard about. It's called *Pig Latin*. Pig Latin is a language code that's fun to speak. This is how it works.

When a word begins with a vowel letter, like *a* or *e*, you add *way* to the end of the word. For example, the word *and* would become *andway* in Pig Latin.

If a word begins with a single consonant, like *b* or *d* or *s*, you put that letter at the end of the word. Then you add *ay* to it. For example, the word *say* would become *aysay*. The word *dig* would be *igday*.

272

If a word begins with two consonants, like *ch*, *sl*, or *br*, you move both letters to the end of the word. Then you add *ay*. For example, the word *chair* would become *airchay*. The word *slam* would be *amslay*. The word *bread* would be *eadbray*.

Pig Latin is a language that everyone has a good time using. It sounds mysterious to those who don't know it. But Pig Latin is really fun for those who do.

See if you can decode this message written in Pig Latin:

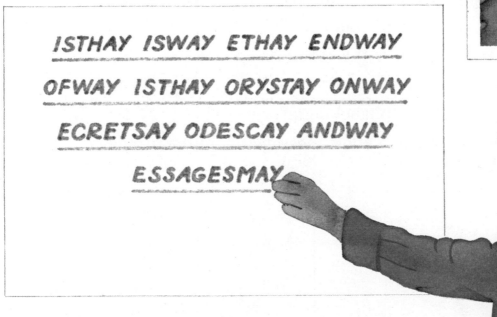

ISTHAY ISWAY ETHAY ENDWAY

OFWAY ISTHAY ORYSTAY ONWAY

ECRETSAY ODESCAY ANDWAY

ESSAGESMAY

If you said, "This is the end of this story on secret codes and messages," you were right!

Comprehension Check

1. What does the word *encoding* mean? What does *decoding* mean?
2. Why do you think the writer of this story says that when you use invisible ink there's more on your paper than meets the eye?
3. Do you think using codes and messages is fun? Explain your answer.
4. Make up a secret code of your own. Then teach it to a friend.

Skill Check

1. What is the first step to follow when using the alphabet code?
2. What is the second step?
3. How do you put both steps together to use the alphabet code?
4. Write a short message using the alphabet code.

Putting Clues Together

Some things in a story are not said. You have to figure them out yourself. In the next story, look for clues that help you figure out what time of year the story takes place.

Jeff and his mother put on their heavy coats. They walked outside into the deep snow. The cold wind blew across the front yard.

The story does not say exactly when the action happened. You need to put together some of the clues. One clue is that Jeff and his mother put on their heavy coats. What are some other clues in the story?

At what time of year does the story take place? If you said winter, you were right.

Practice

Read the story below. This time look for clues that tell you who the storyteller is.

Boy, am I tired. Every afternoon it's the same thing. First Wilma comes home from school. Then she throws me over her shoulder and takes me outside. She takes off her shoes. Then she puts me on her feet. Ouch! She always ties me a little too tight. Soon we're off, rolling down the street.

1. What or who do you think the storyteller is?
2. What clues in the story helped you guess the answer?

Read the next story, "The Alligator Under the Bed." Use the clues to figure out things in the story that are not said.

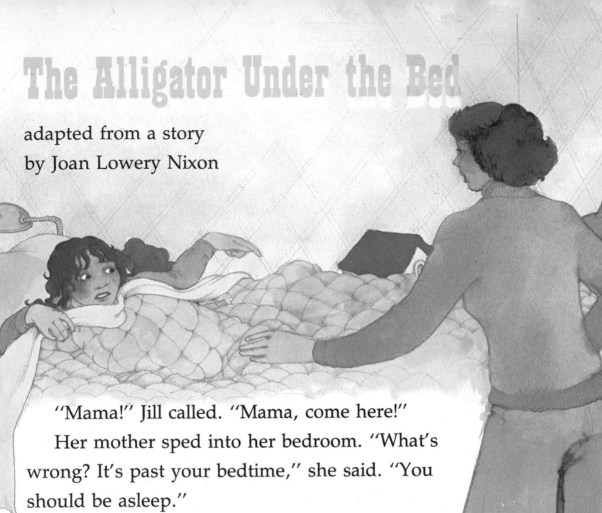

The Alligator Under the Bed

adapted from a story
by Joan Lowery Nixon

"Mama!" Jill called. "Mama, come here!"

Her mother sped into her bedroom. "What's wrong? It's past your bedtime," she said. "You should be asleep."

Jill tugged her blanket up to her neck. "There's an alligator under my bed," she said softly.

"Now, now, Jill," said her mother. "I expect you just had a dream. Go to sleep, dear."

She walked out of the bedroom and back to the living room.

The alligator snorted with glee. Jill could hear his sharp teeth *click, click, clicking* together.

Jill's hands felt icy cold. She was really frightened.

"Papa!" she called. "Papa, I need you!"

Her father sped into the room. "What's the matter, honey? Can't you sleep?" he asked.

Jill drew the blanket up past her neck and covered her nose. "I can't sleep because there's a big alligator hiding under my bed!" she whispered softly.

"Now, now, dear," her father said. "You must have had a bad dream. How could an alligator get under your bed? There's hardly enough room. Try to stop worrying and soon you'll be fast asleep."

He gave her a hug. Then he went back to the living room.

278

Again the alligator snorted with glee.
Again Jill could hear his sharp teeth *click,
click, clicking* together. Her hands got icy
cold again. She was even more frightened than
before. She knew she was not having a dream.
She would *never* dream about alligators. She
kept still as long as she could. Then she
howled:

"Help! I'm frightened! There's an alligator
under my bed!"

Soon Uncle Harry was standing in the doorway
to her bedroom.

"I heard strange noises coming from this
room," he said.

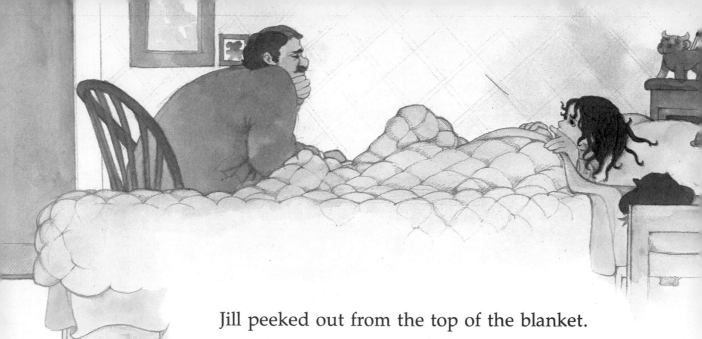

Jill peeked out from the top of the blanket.

"It's the alligator," she whispered softly.

Uncle Harry shoved some extra pillows aside and sat down.

"So that's where he is," he said.

"Who?" Jill asked.

"The alligator. His name is George, isn't it?" said Uncle Harry.

"No," Jill said. "I think his name is Alberta."

Uncle Harry smiled. "Well, I never was any good at remembering names," he said. "But I believe we're talking about the same alligator. Does this one click his teeth and snort with glee?"

"Yes, yes!" exclaimed Jill. "But why is he under my bed?"

"He thinks it makes a good hiding place," Uncle Harry said. "And it's a good thing you found him."

"Why?" Jill asked, slowly pulling the blanket down a drop.

"Simple," Uncle Harry pointed out. "When people lose something special like an alligator, naturally they want him back."

Jill sat up in bed. "I never realized he was lost. Who lost him?" she asked.

"His family," said Uncle Harry. "Isn't it sad that he's here, hiding under your bed, when he should really be home reading bedtime stories to his children?"

Jill thought a moment. "We better tell him to go home," she said.

"That's a good idea," Uncle Harry replied. "*You* tell him because it's your bed he's under."

Jill slowly peeked under the bed. It was very dark and very hard to see the alligator.

"Go home, Alberta!" she shouted. "It's bedtime. Your family wants to hear a bedtime story. They want you home right this minute!"

She sat up and looked at Uncle Harry. "He wants to stay under the bed," she said.

282

Uncle Harry stood up. "The problem with alligators," he exclaimed, pointing to the one under the bed, "is that they are very proud. They don't like you to know they can't do something. Alberta is too proud to tell you that he doesn't know how to open the front door."

"You could do it for him," Jill said.

"Good idea," Uncle Harry replied. He walked to the door. "Come with me, Alberta," he said.

"Wait," Jill cried. She thought again. "He can't go with you. He's a big alligator, and he's caught under the bed."

"Of course he's caught. I should have thought of that," Uncle Harry said.

Uncle Harry reached under the bed and began to tug and tug and tug. Jill slowly moved down to the foot of her bed to watch.

"What are you doing?" she asked.

"I'm tugging him out," Uncle Harry said.

Suddenly he hopped back and caught himself against the door.

"There! He's not stuck now!" said Uncle Harry.

"You got him out?" Jill asked. "He's really not stuck anymore?"

"Right," Uncle Harry replied. "And now he's going back home to his own family. By now they must realize he's gone. Why don't you stand in the doorway and watch Alberta follow me down the hall?"

Jill hopped out of bed and stood in the doorway. Uncle Harry snapped his fingers once. Then he snapped his fingers again. Soon he had snapped himself and Alberta all the way down the hall.

Jill hurried down the hall too. She heard the front door open and her father ask, "What are you doing?"

"I'm sending the alligator home," Uncle Harry said, snapping his fingers one last time.

Then suddenly his voice changed and he sounded a little angry.

"Good-by, Alberta," he said, shoving the alligator out the door. "Good-by! Don't you come back and try those tricks on us again!"

The front door closed.

Jill sped back into her bedroom. As she did, she heard her father laugh and say, "Harry, you and Jill are two of a kind."

She hopped into bed. Then she saw Uncle Harry peeking in the doorway.

"Uncle Harry," she asked, "what did Papa mean when he said we were two of a kind?"

"Hmmmm . . . Maybe he thinks we look just alike," Uncle Harry said.

Jill looked at Uncle Harry's mustache. Then she looked at his round, fat tummy. She couldn't help but giggle a little. She realized that couldn't be why.

Jill thought for a moment. Then suddenly she knew the answer.

"I know!" she exclaimed, feeling very proud of herself. "Papa thinks we're two of a kind because *we* knew what to do about Alberta."

"I expect you're right," Uncle Harry said, smiling. "I expect you're right."

He fixed Jill's blanket so she would be warm as toast. Then he leaned over and whispered, "Good night."

Comprehension Check

1. Why did Jill say she couldn't fall asleep?
2. Why do you think that Jill's mother and father said she must have had a dream?
3. Do you think Jill felt better after Uncle Harry sent the alligator home? Why or why not?
4. What else could Jill have done when she thought there was an alligator under her bed?

Skill Check

1. Do you think there was really an alligator under Jill's bed? What clues in the story make you think as you do?
2. Do you think Jill's Uncle Harry really believed there was an alligator? What clues make you think as you do?

On Your Mark, Get Set, Go!

by Jodie Lampert

Ready? On your mark, get set, go! It's time
to start running. Who is in the race? Lots of
people, both young and old. Running is quickly
becoming one of our most popular pastimes.

What is running? It's part of playing tag
and hide-and-seek. It's getting around the
bases in baseball or softball. But it's also
much more. Running is a wonderful form of
exercise and a popular sport.

As an exercise, running helps to keep people
in shape. Keeping in shape means staying
healthy. More people are running to keep in
shape now than ever before.

As a sport, running is exciting to do and beautiful to watch. It's also something you can do with a friend or by yourself.

Racing is a popular form of running. It's a sport in which people compete with one another. They compete to see who can run the fastest. Some races, called *dashes,* cover short distances. Other races, like *marathons,* cover long distances.

In a marathon, runners run more than twenty-six miles. Usually people like to run marathons in cool weather. Cool weather makes it easier for runners to run long distances. Marathons are held in many cities. They are a kind of friendly competition. Runners travel all over the country to compete in them.

    Another popular form of running is jogging. *Jogging* means running at a comfortable and steady pace. How fast you jog is really up to you. In jogging the only person you're competing with is yourself. Competing with yourself means improving a little bit each time you go out and jog. For example, you may jog fifteen minutes each day for one week. The next week you may go out and jog seventeen minutes each day. This means you have improved your jogging time by two minutes. Other joggers may run longer and faster than you. But that's not important. When you jog the main idea is to improve yourself.

When you race or jog, it's important to prepare with warm-ups. *Warm-ups* are exercises that help keep your body loose and healthy so that you can run better and not get hurt.

Marathon runners must be careful. They must begin to prepare for a marathon race at least a year ahead of time. To do this they may run as much as ten miles a day.

Joggers and runners prepare by doing stretching exercises. One kind of stretching exercise is to try to touch your toes without bending your knees. This exercise is always done slowly and carefully. Another stretching exercise is called "reaching for the sky." To do this you must stand on your toes. Then you put your hands above your head and reach up as high as you can.

To race or run a marathon, you must be very healthy. It's a good idea to check with a doctor to make sure you're in good enough shape. Other people can also help you. Coaches and special trainers can give you good advice about how to prepare for a race.

Racing and marathon running are difficult sports. They may not be for everyone. Jogging and running just for fun are different. They are sports most of us can enjoy. So, if you want to give them a try, put on a good pair of sneakers or running shoes. Make sure to do some warm-up exercises. Then get ready, get set, go out there, and run!

Comprehension Check

1. What are the different forms of running?
2. How many miles a day do some marathon runners run?
3. Why do you think running helps keep a person in shape?
4. Explain how to do the exercise called "reaching for the sky." What kind of exercise is it?
5. Why do you think some people enjoy running a short race? Why do you think some people enjoy running a marathon?

Skill Check

Look at the words below. Answer these questions for each word:
1. What is the suffix?
2. What is the root word?

quickly wonderful
beautiful usually
friendly careful

The Great Blueness and Other Predicaments

by Arnold Lobel

Long ago there were no colors in the world at
all. Almost everything was grey, and what was
not grey was black or white. It was a time that
was called The Great Greyness.

Every morning a Wizard who lived during the time of The Great Greyness would open his window and look out at the wide land. "Something is very wrong with the world," he would say. "It is hard to tell when the rainy days stop and the sunny days begin."

The Wizard would often go down the stairs to his dark, grey cellar. There, just to amuse himself, he would make wonderful magic potions and spells.

One day while the Wizard was mixing and stirring a little of this and a bit of that, he saw something strange in the bottom of his pot.

"What good-looking stuff I have made!" he exclaimed. "I will make some more right away."

296

"What is it?" asked the neighbors when they saw the Wizard painting his house.

"A color," said the Wizard. "I call it *blue*."

"Please," cried the neighbors, "please give us some!"

"Of course," said the Wizard.

And that was how The Great Blueness came to be. After a short time everything in the world was blue.

Trees were blue. Bees were blue. Wheels and evening meals were blue. The Wizard would pedal out on his blue bicycle to look around at the wide, blue world. He would say, "What a perfect day we are having."

But The Blueness was not so perfect. After a long time all that blue made everyone sad. Children played no games. They sulked in their blue backyards. Mothers and fathers sat at home and stared gloomily at the blue pictures on the walls of their blue living rooms.

"Nobody laughs anymore," said the Wizard. "Even I myself have not smiled for days. I must do something," he said as he slouched down to his dark, blue cellar.

There he began to mix and stir a little of
this and a bit of that. Soon he saw something
new in the bottom of his pot.

"Now here is happier stuff," said the Wizard.
"I will make some more right away."

"What is that?" asked the neighbors when they
saw the Wizard painting his fence.

"I am calling it *yellow*," said the Wizard.

"May we have some?" begged the neighbors.

"You may," replied the Wizard.

And that was how The Great Yellowness came to be. After a short time everything in the world was yellow. There was not a flyspeck of blue anywhere to be seen.

Pigs were yellow. Wigs were yellow. Stairs and dentist chairs were yellow. The Wizard would gallop out on his yellow horse to explore the wide, yellow world. He would say, "What a fine day we are having."

But The Yellowness was not so fine. After a long time all that yellow began to hurt everyone's eyes. People walked about bumping and thumping into each other. They were squinting and could not see where they were going.

"This Yellowness is too bright and blinding," moaned the Wizard, who had a cold towel on his head. "Everyone has a headache, and so do I."

So the Wizard stumbled down the stairs to his dark, yellow cellar. There he mixed and stirred a little of this and a bit of that. Soon he saw something different in the bottom of his pot.

"This is handsome stuff," declared the Wizard. "I will make some more right away."

"What do you call that?" asked the neighbors when they saw the Wizard painting his flowers.

"*Red*," answered the Wizard.

"We would like some too," pleaded the neighbors.

"Right away," said the Wizard.

And that was how The Great Redness came to be. After a short time everything in the world was red.

Mountains were red. Fountains were red. Limburger cheese and afternoon teas were red. The Wizard would sail out in his red boat to see what he could see of the wide, red world. He would say, "What a glorious day we are having."

But The Redness was not so glorious. After a long time all that red put everyone into a very bad temper. So the Wizard stormed down the stairs to his dark, red cellar. He mixed and stirred for many days. He used all the magic that he could think of to find a new color, but all that he made was more and more blue, more and more yellow, and more and more red. The Wizard worked until all of his pots were filled to the top.

The pots were so full that they soon overflowed. The blue and the yellow and the red all began to mix together. It was a terrible mess. But when the Wizard saw what was happening, he exclaimed, "That is the answer!" And he danced joyfully around the cellar.

The Wizard mixed the red with the blue and made a new color. The Wizard mixed the yellow with the blue and made a new color. The Wizard mixed the yellow with the red and made a new color.

"Hurrah!" he shouted, and he mixed the red and the blue and the yellow in all kinds of different ways.

"Look at these beautiful things I have made!" said the Wizard when he was finished.

"What are they?" asked the neighbors.

"I call them *purple* and *green* and *orange* and *brown*," said the Wizard.

"They are a sight for sore eyes," cried the neighbors. "But which one shall we choose this time?"

"You must take them all," said the Wizard.

The people did take all the colors the Wizard had made. After a short time they found good places for each one.

After a long time when the Wizard opened his window, he would look out and say, "What a perfectly fine and glorious day we are having."

The neighbors brought the Wizard gifts of red apples and green leaves and yellow bananas and purple grapes and blue flowers.

At last the world was too beautiful ever to be changed again.

WHAT IS PINK?

by Christina Rossetti

What is pink? A rose is pink
By the fountain's brink.
What is red? A poppy's red
In its barley bed.
What is blue? The sky is blue
Where the clouds float through.
What is white? A swan is white
Sailing in the light.
What is yellow? Pears are yellow,
Rich and ripe and mellow.
What is green? The grass is green,
With small flowers between.
What is violet? Clouds are violet
In the summer twilight.
What is orange? Why, an orange,
Just an orange!

Glossary

arrow 1.

bluff 1.

A a

amuse **1.** keep pleased and interested: *Amuse yourself while I'm gone.* **2.** cause to laugh or smile: *The puppy amused us.* **amused, amus ing.**

ar row **1.** a sign used to show a direction on maps and roads. See the picture. **2.** a kind of pointed stick.

B b

bluff **1.** a hill that rises straight up from the ground. See the picture. **2.** pretend to be sure of one's self. **bluffs; bluffed, bluff ing.**

brood er **1.** a box in which baby birds are placed in order to help them grow. **2.** a person who worries about something all the time. **brood ers.**

C c

case **1.** something that can hold something else: *The violin is in its case.* See the picture. **2.** a box: *There is a case of canned fruit in the basement.* **cas es.**

cos tume special clothes: *In our play Pete wore a king's costume.* See the picture. **cos tumes.**

co-work er a person who works along with another person on a job: *My co-worker and I painted the room together.* **co-work ers.**

cudd ly nice to hug and hold close: *My teddy bear is soft and cuddly.*

D d

dash **1.** rush: *They dashed down the street to catch the bus.* **2.** a little bit: *We put a dash of salt in the soup.* **dashed, dash ing; dash es.**

duck **1.** bend the body quickly so as to get out of the way: *I ducked under the covers so my dog would not find me.* See the picture. **2.** dip the head or body under water. **3.** a swimming bird. **ducked, duck ing; ducks.**

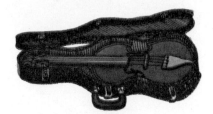

case 1.

costume

duck 1.

E e

ed i tor a person in charge of a magazine, book, or newspaper who decides what will be printed in it. **ed i tors.**

ex claim speak or cry out suddenly with strong feeling: *"Go, team, go!" Rosa exclaimed as her team scored a point.* **ex claimed, ex claim ing.**

ex hib it 1. a place where things are shown. See the picture. **2.** present or show something for people to see: *At the fair I will exhibit the stamps I collected.* **ex hib it ed, ex hib it ing.**

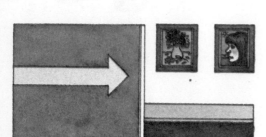

exhibit 1.

flight 1.

F f

flight 1. a set of stairs leading from one floor of a building to the next: *We live one flight up.* See the picture. **2.** a ride in an airplane: *Miles took the first flight to New York.* **3.** running away: *Their flight from the storm brought them to a safe place.* **flights.**

flute a musical instrument that you play by blowing into it and pressing keys. See the picture. **flutes.**

flute

G g

gi ant **1.** in stories, a person of great size. See the picture. **2.** huge: *a giant sandwich.* **gi ants.**

gig gle **1.** laugh in a silly way: *He giggled when he saw the funny picture.* **2.** a silly laugh. **gig gled, gig gling; gig gles.**

grouch a person who is not happy and is sometimes not nice to other people. **grouch es.**

H h

ham mer **1.** a tool used to hit nails into wood. See the picture. **2.** hit with a hammer: *She hammered the nails into the wood.* **ham mers; ham mered, ham mer ing.**

hatch **1.** come out of an egg: *One chicken hatched today.* See the picture. **2.** plan secretly; plot: *The class was hatching a surprise for their teacher.* **hatched, hatch ing.**

hip po pot a mus a big animal that lives in or near water. See the picture. **hip po pot a mus es** or **hip po pot a mi.**

giant

hippopotamus

giant   1.

hammer   1.

hatch   1.

hippopotamus

hon ey a thick, sweet, yellow liquid that is good to eat. Bees make honey from the drops they collect from flowers. **hon eys.**

ink

I i

ink the colored liquid used in a pen: *Luis's pen wrote with blue ink.* See the picture.

J j

jog **1.** a slow, steady run. **2.** run slowly. See the picture. **jogged, jog ging.**

juice the liquid part of fruit or vegetables or meat. **juic es.**

jog 2.

K k

keep er a person who watches over or takes care of persons, animals, or things. **keep ers.**

knot **1.** strings or ropes tied together so that they will not pull apart. See the picture. **2.** tie in a knot: *Knot the string so it won't slip.* **knots; knot ted, knot ting.**

knot 1.

L l

let ter **1.** a mark or sign that stands for any one of the sounds that are in words: *There are 26 letters in our alphabet.* **2.** a written message: *Juanita wrote her friend a letter.* See the picture. **let ters.**

lone ly feeling sad and wanting other people to be with you: *Lisa felt lonely because she had no one to play with.* **lone li er, lone li est.**

letter 2.

M m

mar a thon **1.** a foot race of about 26 miles (about 42 kilometers). See the picture. **2.** any long race or contest. **mar a thons.**

marathon 1.

N n

nail **1.** a small, pointed piece of metal that can be hammered into pieces of wood to hold them together. **2.** the hard part at the end of a finger or toe. See the picture. **nails.**

nail 2.

311

newsstand

ostrich

parrot

nerv ous very excited and worried: *Sam was nervous because he had to take a test.* **nerv ous ly.**

news stand a place where newspapers and magazines are sold. See the picture. **news stands.**

O o

---

om e let eggs prepared in a special way. An omelet often has other foods inside, such as cheese, jelly, or ham. **om e lets.**

os trich a large, long-legged bird that can run fast but cannot fly. See the picture. **os trich es.**

P p

---

pa rade many people marching, sometimes with musical instruments and flags: *The clowns were in the circus parade.* **pa rades.**

par rot a brightly colored bird. Some parrots can be taught to say words. See the picture. **par rots.**

pave cover a road with concrete or tar and make it smooth. **paved, pav ing.**

Q q

ques tion a sentence asked to find something out: *The teacher asked Chan a question.* **ques tions.**

R r

re fresh ment something to eat or drink: *Sara bought refreshments in the park.* See the picture. **re fresh ments.**

re ward **1.** something given for something done. **2.** give a reward to: *Mrs. O'Malley rewarded Norman for finding her cat.* **re wards; re ward ed, re ward ing.**

roll **1.** move along by turning over and over: *The pencil rolled under the desk.* **2.** a kind of bread: *sweet roll.* See the picture. **rolled, roll ing; rolls.**

refreshment

roll 2.

S s

scoop **1.** a story gotten for a newspaper or magazine before other reporters get it. **2.** a large, deep spoon used to serve food. See the picture. **scoops.**

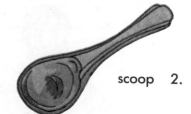

scoop 2.

313

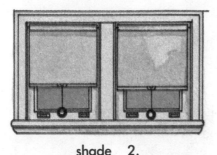

shade 2.

sea son **1.** one of the four parts of the year; spring, summer, fall, or winter. **2.** improve the taste of something: *The soup was seasoned with salt and pepper.* **sea sons; sea soned, sea son ing.**

shade **1.** a place not in the bright sun: *It is quite cool in the shade.* **2.** something that shuts out light: *Pull down the shade if you don't want the sun in your eyes.* See the picture. **shades.**

shud der shake your body suddenly from either fear or cold: *Laura began to shudder from the cold.* **shud dered, shud der ing.**

T t

theater

tie 2.

tar something black and sticky that comes from wood or coal: *The workers are paving the street with tar.*

the a ter a place where plays are acted out or movies are shown. See the picture. **the a ters.**

tie **1.** wrap with a string or rope: *Please tie these boxes together.* **2.** a piece of clothing worn around the neck: *Jim always wears a striped tie.* See the picture. **3.** having the same score: *The ball game ended in a tie.* **tied, ty ing; ties.**

trunk 1. the lower and thicker part of a tree. See the picture. **2.** an elephant's nose. **3.** a big box used for carrying clothes when traveling. **trunks.**

tu ba a musical instrument that you play by blowing into it and pressing the keys. It has a deep tone. See the picture. **tu bas.**

U u

---

usual ly most of the time: *Kenneth is usually hungry at lunchtime.*

V v

---

vi o lin a musical instrument that you play by moving a bow across strings. See the picture. **vi o lins.**

W w

---

wher ev er any place at all: *Sit wherever you would like.*

wink close and open one eye as a signal. See the picture. **winked, wink ing.**

trunk 1.

tuba

violin

wink

wizard
***
zookeeper

wizard

xylophone

yucca

wiz ard in stories, a person said to have magical powers. See the picture. **wiz ards.**

Wy o ming one of the fifty states of the United States. It is in the western part of the United States.

X x

xy lo phone a musical instrument. You play it by hitting metals bars with small hammers. See the picture. **xy lo phones.**

Y y

yuc ca a green plant that grows in warm areas. It has pointed leaves and whitish flowers. See the picture. **yuc cas.**

Z z

zoo a place where wild animals are kept for people to see. **zoos.**

zoo keep er a person who takes care of the animals at the zoo. **zoo keep ers.**

MASTERY WORD LIST

The following words have been read enough times for pupils to reach mastery by the end of this book. Pupils should be able to recognize both the root word and the root word with these endings, suffixes, and spelling changes: *s, es, ed, ing, 's, er, est, en; ful, ly*; final consonant doubled, final *e* dropped, final *y* changed to *i*. The number after each word shows the page on which the word first appears as a mastery word in this book. For a cumulative list see the Teacher's Edition for *Crystal Kingdom*.

bottle 8	lonely 23	beneath 45	shook 62
camel 8	bus 24	instrument 50	concert 63
dime 8	inside 24	language 50	board 64
genie 8	quietly 24	music 50	hurry 64
imagination 8	shut 24	spoken 50	somewhere 64
imagine 8	turn 26	whistle 50	exactly 65
wonderful 8	dark 27	imitate 51	fit 67
Sunday 9	suddenly 27	musical 51	birthday 72
basement 10	crawl 29	blow 52	gift 72
pipe 10	noise 29	bongo 52	invite 72
awful 11	been 33	flute 52	party 72
fill 11	hello 34	string 52	broke 73
flood 11	tire 34	violin 52	grin 73
plumber 11	good-by 36	direction 53	surprise 73
rush 11	supper 36	rhythm 53	cake 74
worry 11	extra 37	tube 54	act 75
yell 11	favorite 37	pencil 56	lesson 75
dry 12	turnip 37	rubber 56	tuba 75
bush 22	vegetable 37	arm 59	rang 76
footstep 22	kitchen 38	orchestra 59	aunt 77
heard 22	omelet 38	trombone 59	ring 77
sidewalk 22	dessert 39	older 60	snapper 77
beside 23	o'clock 41	practice 60	joy 80
explain 23	sweep 41	tiptoe 60	job 88

cover 221
print 221
sport 221
star 221
plan 222
reader 222
fact 223
figure 223
issue 224
writer 224
check 225
edit 225
artist 226
paste 227
breath 230
exclaim 231
deliver 232
newsstand 232
quickly 233
sped 233
flash 234
grumpy 234
printer 234
copy 239
elephant 245
reply 245
sign 245
apple 246
iced 246
juice 246
point 246
refreshment 246
shoulder 246
pretend 247
bag 248
peanut 248
seal 248
washroom 249
bench 250
slowly 253
stair 253
stew 253
stir 253
avenue 254
realize 254
softly 254
bookmobile 255
chair 255
continue 255
shelves 258
howl 259
trunk 262
autumn 263
icy 263
travel 263
code 266
communicate 266
decode 266
detective 266
message 266
example 267
letter 267
exchange 268
instead 268
ink 269
invisible 269
bulb 270
pig 272
alligator 277
bedtime 277
blanket 277
click 277
dream 277
expect 277
glee 277
snort 277
tug 277
doorway 279
peek 280
caught 283
hop 284
finger 285
exercise 289
form 289
healthy 289
popular 289
race 289
shape 289
compete 290
distance 290
marathon 290
runner 290
yourself 290
improve 291
jog 291
jogger 292
prepare 292
stretch 292

A separate group of skill-related words appears below. Pupils will be able to recognize these terms.

paragraph 20
practice 20
comprehension 32
skill 32
r-controlled 46
vowel 46
consonant 47
alphabetical order 85
dictionary 85
entry word 85
glossary 85
definition 86
details 123
main idea 188
guide word 219
root word 241

(Acknowledgments continued from page 2)

"Neighbors" from HELLO AND GOOD-BYE by Mary Ann Hoberman. Copyright © 1959 by Mary Ann Hoberman. Reprinted by permission of Russell & Volkening, Inc. as agents for the author.

"Eddie Couldn't Find the Elephants" adapted from EDDIE COULDN'T FIND THE ELEPHANTS © 1974 by Edith Battles. Used with permission of Albert Whitman & Company.

"A Quiet Place" adapted from A QUIET PLACE by Rose Blue. Copyright © 1969 by Rose Bluestone. Used by permission of the publisher, Franklin Watts, Inc.

"At the Library" is reprinted by permission of E. P. Dutton from RHYMES ABOUT US by Marchette Chute. Copyright © 1974 by Marchette Chute.

Adapted by permission of G. P. Putnam's Sons from THE ALLIGATOR UNDER THE BED by Joan Lowery Nixon. Copyright © 1974 by Joan Lowery Nixon.

"The Great Blueness and Other Predicaments" contains the abridged text and selected illustrations from THE GREAT BLUENESS AND OTHER PREDICAMENTS, written and illustrated by Arnold Lobel. Copyright © 1968 by Arnold Lobel. By permission of Harper & Row, Publishers, Inc. and World's Work Ltd., The Windmill Press.

Glossary entries and skill lesson dictionary entries taken or adapted from MY SECOND PICTURE DICTIONARY. Copyright © 1975, 1971 Scott, Foresman and Company. All Rights Reserved. Also from SCOTT, FORESMAN BEGINNING DICTIONARY. Copyright © 1979 Scott, Foresman and Company, Glenview, Illinois. All Rights Reserved.

ILLUSTRATIONS

Cover: Doug Johnson
Pages 8–17, Catherine Leary; page 18, Lesley Achitoff; pages 19–21, Kathy McCarthy; pages 22–32, Jared Lee; pages 33–46, Judith Chang; pages 47–49, Kathy McCarthy; pages 51–52, Claudia Sargeant; pages 59–71, Daryl Moore; page 71, Allan Eitzen; pages 72–84, Ann Iosa; pages 85–87, Kathy McCarthy; pages 99–109, Catherine Leary; pages 110–121, Judith Chang; page 122, Randi Wasserman; pages 123–124, Kathy McCarthy; pages 130–131, Linda Miyamoto; pages 132–142, June Goldsborough; pages 143–144, Kathy McCarthy; pages 154–164, Paulette Giguere; page 165, Jim Dyekman; page 166, Stella Ormai; pages 168–177, Bruce Lemerise; page 178, Linda Strauss Edwards; pages 179–187, Elliot Kreloff; pages 188–189, Kathy McCarthy; pages 190–200, Jose Reyes; pages 201–207, Catherine Leary; pages 208–216, David Febland; page 217, Angela Adams; page 221, François Colos; pages 230–241, Linda Miyamoto; pages 242–244, Kathy McCarthy; pages 245–252, Linda Miyamoto; pages 253–264, Freya Tanz; page 265, Bob Barner; pages 266–274, Nancy Schill; pages 275–276, Kathy McCarthy; pages 277–288, Pam Ford; pages 295–304, Arnold Lobel; pages 306–316, Claudia Sargeant.

PHOTOGRAPHS

Pages 50–51, 53–57, 88–90, Barbara Kirk; page 91, New York Zoological Society; pages 92, 93 (top), Barbara Kirk; page 93 (bottom), New York Zoological Society; pages 94–98, Barbara Kirk; page 125 (left), Mannau Sassionian, *Editorial Photocolor Archives*; page 125 (right), Peter Vadnai, *Editorial Photocolor Archives*; page 126 (top left), Susan McCartney, *Photo Researchers*; page 126 (top right), Jack Fields, *Photo Researchers*; page 126 (bottom left), Adam Woolfitt, *Woodfin Camp & Associates*; page 126 (bottom right), SCALA, *Editorial Photocolor Archives*; page 127 (middle), L. L. Smith, *Photo Researchers*; page 127 (right), Timothy Eagan, *Woodfin Camp & Associates*; page 128 (left), Timothy Eagan, *Woodfin Camp & Associates*; page 128 (right), Adam Woolfitt, *Woodfin Camp & Associates*; page 129, George Holton, *Photo Researchers*; pages 145–153, 221–229, 289–294, Barbara Kirk; page 305, Bud McLouth.

STUDIO

Educational Graphics, Inc.